SOULS ON FIRE

MEMOIRS OF A TWIN FLAME TRUE LOVE JOURNEY

MICHELLE WHITE | JUSTIN WHITE

Copyright © 2021 by Divine Love Enterprises LLC

All rights reserved.

No part of this book may be reproduced in any form or by any electronic or mechanical means, including information storage and retrieval systems, without written permission from the author, except for the use of brief quotations in a book review.

Cover design by Silvana G. Sánchez © SP Designs
www.selfpubdesigns.com

❀ Created with Vellum

This story is dedicated to <u>you</u>.

May you find what you're looking for.

PART II

If you don't like the role you landed,
flip the script.

CHAPTER 1

September 2015

*A*fter casing your neighborhood, I parked on the opposite side of the street two blocks down from your tan house. Eyes trained on the sliver of it visible from this angle, I settled in to wait under the cotton ball-dotted late-summer sky of the Pacific Northwest. For the twentieth time, I debated whether or not this was a good idea. Scabbed cuticles beckoned. My phone vibrated, and Ed's face popped up on the screen.

"Hello," I answered, thankful it wasn't ten minutes later.

"Hey, I just found out I'm getting two new clients in the Bay Area, so I'll be spending every other week there the rest of the year. You gonna be okay at home with the kids?"

"Do I have a choice?" I rejoined tartly.

"Shell, of course, there's a choice. I can tell my manager that my trips have to be less frequent, or fewer days at a time. He needs me happy because there's no one to backfill my position if I leave," he paused for a beat. "That would affect my bonus, though." I sighed, trying to release the threadbare anxiety that reared up whenever Ed had to travel.

"I know, I get it," I brushed off his faint offer to decline the opportunity. I didn't want him home anyway.

"Are you at your class yet?" he asked.

"Yeah, about to walk in. Remember, I won't be able to pick up the phone for a couple hours." The line was silent, except for the distinctive ticking of a mouse button. I shouted, "Hello!"

"Uh," I could hear him typing in the background.

"I'm hanging up now!" I huffed.

"Sorry, what were you saying?"

"Never mind!" I shifted my tone to neutral, "I'll be home in time to pick the kids up."

"Sounds good, see you then," we hung up without exchanging 'I love yous.' I returned to my vigil. A few minutes passed. You emerged from your house to drag the garbage and recycling bins to the side yard. I admired you from afar, confident in my invisibility behind the glaring windshield. I jumped when you reappeared, looked straight at me, and checked your watch. A prescription bottle materialized in my hand. Two tablets joined the pharmaceutical soup swirling in my stomach. You went back inside.

We'd been together four or five times since our first encounter in July. Until today, I insisted you follow the same rules as the rest of the men I spent time with; you must come to me. I felt protected in my home environment, though there was no real safety in it. You complied cheerfully. However, your inconsistent schedule, like anyone's in the retail service sector, made it tough for you to set aside a big enough chunk of hours to drive to me, spend time with me, and return home. I enjoyed more latitude as a stay-at-home-mom, so I agreed to meet you at your house. Glancing in the rearview mirror, I was surprised not to see a police cruiser. Guilt gurgled in my stomach.

My cuticles beckoned again, but I was too afraid of leaving bloodstains on your bedsheets to dig in. I picked at one that looked unlikely to open up and decided today would be our last time together. Every man I had an affair with had a shelf-life; few were awarded the privilege of being with me twice, let alone many times.

Every man, except for you.

Watching seconds tick down, I wondered why. Perhaps because you didn't bombard me with texts and emails like the others, who seemed so worried that my initial 'yes' would become a 'no' before they could notch me into their belt. You were quieter. Your brand of carrying on an affair was almost respectful. Though I'd wanted to laugh when you thanked me after our first time together, I came to realize that you really meant it. You'd been thanking me for seeing you, for spending time with you, for sharing my body with you. *I* knew what we were doing was wrong. *You* knew what we were doing was wrong. The paradoxes unsettled me. Nevertheless, I kept inviting you back, more often than any other man besides my Canadian hockey player.

Time was up.

I texted you, "I'm here."

You texted back, "Okay." I waited. When instructions were not forthcoming, I texted again.

"What should I do?"

"Come to the front door. Dog might bark, but she won't hurt you." The nerves around my stomach fluttered, highlighting the pressure I felt in my bladder. The drive had taken over an hour, and I was in desperate need of a toilet. I hesitated, questioning again whether or not this was a good idea. Another text arrived.

"Where are you? I don't see your car," it read.

"I'm pulling up now," I hit send and started the engine. I eased away from the curb, crept down the street, and parked by your crinkly dead-grass lawn. I gulped a mouthful of water before exiting the safety of the car. When I peeked around the corner of the garage, I saw the front door propped open an inch. No one was there. A pointy black nose poked out of the door crack, just above my knee height. A slice of your face appeared a few feet above it, then slid down to reveal the crown of your honey blonde head. As you backed away, you swung open the door to admit me. I stepped across the threshold, all concerns about potential danger swept away with the tide of anti-anxiety drugs turning in my nervous system.

"Hey," I greeted. You let go of your dog's collar and straightened to kiss me. After a peck, you watched her.

"I can't believe what I see," your eyes were round. She circled me, sniffing. I crouched in a low squat to peer into her face. She nervously wagged her tail when I reached for her. As soon as my palms smoothed her long-haired rat terrier coat, she melted.

"What're you seeing?" I smiled up at you.

"Sissy goes nuts when strangers come over," you informed me. "She's never been so calm meeting a new person. Never!"

"Pets usually like me," I shrugged it off. Sissy wedged herself between my knees and nudged my idle fingers. I rubbed her head and ruffled her back fur, then stood. Your gaze alternated between your dog and me.

"So strange she didn't bark," you paused on me, squinting as if to see me in better focus. I cleared my throat, uncomfortable with the scrutiny.

"Is it okay if I use the bathroom?" I asked.

"Sure, follow me," you sprung into motion, preceding me through the living room and kitchen before turning left down a short hallway. A sickly sweet smell hung in the air, and I felt my sinuses react.

"Today is definitely our last day! No way I'm coming back to this," I thought, eyes watering. You showed me into a mostly-clean bathroom that was obviously the domain of a teenage male. "Thanks," I said.

"I'll wait in the kitchen," you pointed back the way we came. As I used the facilities, I prepared myself

7

mentally for our farewell fuck. That was how I'd come to think of these trysts over the past few months; they were just the fucks I did between walking the kids to school and picking them up in the afternoon. The word rung hollow today. What you and I did together didn't seem as crass as the 'fucking' I did with all the others. When we were together, the mystical ease with which my orgasms arrived still confounded me.

"I bet today I don't even have an orgasm," I wagered against myself in the mirror, trying to drum up excitement for ditching you. My heart, where I liked to cultivate a sad ache before I twisted the knife in a doomed lover's breast, was stubbornly silent. I rolled my eyes at my reflection and straightened the hand towel. I went to find you in the kitchen.

"Hi, again," you greeted as I sidled up to claim a real hello kiss. Your arms encircled me, and our tongues entwined. I felt as breathless as ever when we were close. You pulled back, grabbed my hand, and said, "Come on." I let you lead me toward the bedroom you shared with your wife. I paused on the threshold to look at the bed. You'd spread it over with white woven blankets, and I flashed upon a dream or memory of some formal tribal deflowering rite. I shook my head. Your room burst back into focus through the dark overlay of my vision.

"Too much Xanax," I thought as I let you tug me further into your lair.

"Come here," you pulled me into your arms again, and we tangled together, stripping clothes as we went. I wore the hot pink panty set. You seemed to relish seeing it on my bulbous body, and I liked to please the men I fucked. When you paused to admire me, Sissy leaped onto the bed.

"Sissy, no," you commanded. "Get down!"

"Let her stay," I said. "I don't mind and, look, she just wants to lie down near us." She was indeed spinning in a circle. She settled into a donut of black-and-white-and-tan fur on the far side of the king mattress. Your attention returned to me, and I felt the insistence of your erection between us. We collapsed onto the white blankets and lost ourselves in each other.

CHAPTER 2

Two years earlier…

"What happened after the CEO adjourned the meeting?" Dr. Drexler asked. We faced each other in a white exam room, where she'd been listening to me talk for an hour. Indian summer hadn't yet begun baking Silicon Valley. Still, it loomed along with the school year that would take Eddie into fourth grade and Elsie into first. We'd been home from Hawaii a week. The kids were tan, brimming with tales of slurping shave ice and dodging fire-worms on the beach at our resort. Ed started back to work the morning after we landed at SFO. I tacked on a short staycation to catch up on the back-to-school crunch. Days were packed, chock-full of chores and schemes to avoid my boss Monica, who knew I was back on the mainland.

I wasn't ready to return to work. The closer that day approached, the stronger my desire to put it off grew. Dread began to choke me when I tried to sleep at night. I found it increasingly impossible to get out of bed in the morning, my mind halting and catching fire in a flurry of what-ifs that I couldn't answer but also couldn't stop asking.

"Michelle, what happened after you ran out?" Dr. Drexler prompted. I wrinkled my brow. She kept her eyes on me but leaned back to give me time. I didn't want to think about the days following the meeting in which Jay scapegoated me a month ago. Anxiety seized me, and I clenched my teeth tight.

"They didn't fire you, did they?" she prodded. "Because if they did—"

"No," I broke through the lockjaw. "Jay left for vacation the next day. Monica let me work from home. Since the acquisition program was officially on hiatus due to the blunder with the rating agencies, everyone took a step back to recuperate."

"Gee, I wonder why!" the doctor exclaimed, uncharacteristically sarcastic. "Tell me what happened when Jay got back from vacation."

"Well, I played musical appointments with Jay's assistant, Penny, until we left for Hawaii. I was trying to get in to see him so we could plan the rating agency relations overhaul he sprung on me," I shuddered. "As usual, my appointment kept getting shuffled around. Finally, one time when I tried to reschedule, Penny lost her temper," I started to hyperventilate.

Dr. Drexler leaned over to pass me a box of tissues from the countertop, asking, "What on earth for?"

"She — she —" I stuttered. With flat palms, I squeezed either side of my ribcage, imagining all my hurt feelings squishing into a cube, like trash in a compactor. "She told me that every time Jay saw she'd rescheduled the meeting, he told her to cancel it. She said she felt bad for me, which was why she kept trying, but she wasn't going to do it anymore."

"Oh, Michelle," Dr. Drexler shook her head, eyes closed. My empath sense twinged. It touched off dread that she would tell me to get a new job, like Ed. Or maybe she was going to tell me I was lucky to still have a job, like my mom. Her bright blue eyes popped open, and she said, "Tell me about your vacation. Did Eddie and Elsie have fun?"

"Yeah, they had a blast," I mustered a hint of enthusiasm. Since shortly after Eddie's birth, Dr. Drexler had been our family doctor, caring for our kids like her own two kids who were about a decade older. The last thing I wanted was for her to judge me as a bad parent on top of my career failure. "Eddie discovered SPAM Breakfast at McDonald's, so we drove twelve miles every morning so he could enjoy his food." The doctor laughed appreciatively. She knew Eddie's prodigious food allergies. "Elsie loved the North Shore beaches, so we spent a lot of time there. Oh, and the luau! Somehow, the kids ended up onstage with the dancers," I smiled without happiness. "We went to the pineapple plantation six times for Dole Whip," my eyes clouded over, and the smile melted off of my face.

"It doesn't sound like you enjoyed yourself," Dr. Drexler interpreted. "Why not?"

"I don't know," I dragged my heels. What if she didn't believe me or told me I was being ridiculous? I tried not to sound like I was complaining. "I was fine the first few days! I took a detailed agenda, which we followed to a tee. I left a couple days open at the end so we could do spontaneous activities or revisit the places we loved."

"That was brilliant," Dr. D admired. "I'm gonna do that on our next family trip!" I didn't hear the compliment. I struggled to describe the alien feelings that overwhelmed me on vacation.

My eyes went out-of-focus, and I said, "Something went wrong after we finished everything I planned. I didn't know what to do anymore. It was like my head broke open, and my brain was scooped out," I thumped the side of my skull with my open palm. "I couldn't make one more decision. When Ed and the kids came at me asking what the plan was, I froze. I couldn't *think!*"

"That's not like you," Dr. Drexler observed.

"I know it's not!" It hurt to recall the kids' confused faces and Ed's fumbling attempts to direct the family. I closed my eyes, but the images stayed put.

The doctor asked, "How did you decide what to do from then on?"

"I told Ed, 'I don't know what to do. I can't make another decision,'" I stopped.

"Did he decide?" she drew me out.

Covering my face with my hands, I whispered, "He took us back to the places we already visited." The sobs

I'd kept in check all appointment erupted. Dr. Drexler waited. My tears did not slow.

Finally, she put her hand on my shoulder and said, "Michelle, I'm going to talk to Vi. I'll be back." The door clicked shut. I don't know how much time I sat there alone, berating myself for being stupid, slow, lazy, weak. Dr. Drexler reentered to find me in the same pose as when she left. "Ed's on his way here," she told me.

Surprised, I uncovered my face and asked, "Why?"

"You're not okay, and I don't think you can see it. I need Ed here when I explain," her phone dinged. She glanced at it and said, "He's here." Someone knocked, and Dr. Drexler answered. Ed entered the exam room.

"Thanks, Violet, we'll be out shortly," Dr. Drexler called after her assistant. Ed stood, gaze shifting between the doctor and me. "Have a seat," she indicated an empty chair. He perched on the edge. She cleared her throat and said, "Ed, I invited you to join us because I'm gravely concerned about Michelle. Have you noticed anything different about her lately?"

"Yes," Ed answered, watching me. "It seems like Michelle disappeared, and some automaton showed up in her place."

"When did you first notice this change?" Dr. Drexler was looking at Ed, who was still looking at me. I resisted the urge to grab his chin and twist his face toward her.

"About a week ago?" he guessed, infusing his eyes with a silent plea for me to approve. I saw it in my peripheral vision, but I stared straight ahead. "It was almost at the end of the trip," he continued. "Michelle

14

always plans everything so thoroughly! I knew something was wrong when she just stared," he finally glanced at the doctor before darting his eyes back to my face.

"What else have you noticed about Michelle?" she asked.

"She's sad," he sounded lost. I started crying again, more quietly this time. "She cries a lot, and I know she's worried about going back to work. They demand too much of her," he took up my defense. "She has a toxic boss, but she won't listen to my advice and get a new job!"

Heedless of Dr. Drexler's presence, I snarled, "Wisconsin?"

"Shell, that was years ago," Ed reacted. "You've *got* to let it go. It's not my fault you're still working at a place where they mistreat you!"

Dr. Drexler cut in, saying, "Michelle's not in a position to contemplate career changes, Ed. I called you here to tell you that I'm diagnosing her with major depression and generalized anxiety disorder," she sat down at her computer. My brain reeled. I'd been diagnosed with depression before!

A near-forgotten memory of a sultry Carolina summer night many years ago surfaced. Ed and I stood on the porch of a big, white, low-country mansion, shoulder-to-shoulder. I reached out to knock, but my stepmom's cousin opened the door before my knuckles struck.

"WELCOME HOME!" JoDee chirped, gathering me to her ample bosom, which was clad in a red-and-white gingham halter top. Her easy smile lit up as she held me at arms' length. "Aren't you the most beautiful thing? Look at those eyes," she shook her blonde mane and turned to give Ed similar treatment. "Ed, welcome!" Two tow-headed little ones capered around, and a hound bayed.

"Thank you for having us," I was overwhelmed, but I steeled myself to politeness. "This is our first social outing with someone other than Ed's coworkers since we moved here. We appreciate the invitation."

"Psh!" JoDee waved off my words. "What d'you mean, 'thank you?' Y'all are family, and family *does* for each other. When cousin Charlie told me you moved here, I couldn't wait to meet y'all!" Her husband, tow-headed like the kids, joined us in the entryway. He cracked a can of beer and handed it to Ed, then fished one for himself out of the crook of his elbow.

"Howdy," he smiled. "Hi y'all doing?"

"Jay Bee," JoDee scolded. "You're a scamp! Introduce yourself properly, if you please. That goes for you little ones, too," she ran away up the staircase while they obeyed.

"You can call me Jay," he shook Ed's beer-free hand and nodded at me in welcome.

"I'm Junior. You can call me Jay-Jay," piped the little boy with a courtly bow. "I'm seven."

"Are not!" squeaked a miniature JoDee, checking her brother's exuberance. "Y'all won't be seven till next week." Jay-Jay stuck his tongue out at her.

"Cut that out, now," their dad instructed. "Your mama won't like it. Introduce yourself, girly."

"I'm JoDee Lee, I'm five, and I'm going into Kindergarten," she dropped a crisp curtsy. I was unsurprised to hear the handed-down family names. This was the picture of a perfect Southern white family. I tried to calm my nerves; I wanted to make a good impression on my stepmom's cousin. JoDee rejoined us, carrying a tow-headed infant.

"This is Jasmine," she said proudly. "We call her Jazzy. Wanna hold her?" We were all still crowded in the entry, so I shrugged. "Oh, silly me!" JoDee laughed breezily. "Where's my hospitality? Let's go to the living room. You can hold her there."

Ed and I followed the parade of blonde into a room filled with overstuffed leather couches and a big-screen TV. Jay beckoned Ed through the seating area and out the back screen door, presumably to a man cave I was not allowed to tag along to.

"Boys will have their toys," JoDee said after they disappeared. "Jay Bee is a big fisherman. He just started a fishing club. Does Ed fish?"

"No way," I sounded rude. I hadn't meant to, but lately, I'd had trouble modulating my emotions and matching my tone to my meaning. Conscious of my bad manners, I followed up with, "I mean, he's into computers, you know? More of an indoor type." JoDee politely ignored my botched reply.

"Well, if he's not a fisherman, we can take y'all waterskiing sometime! Jay Bee just bought a brand new speedboat, and it's a beaut," we exchanged small talk while I held the baby on my lap. JoDee paced back and forth to the kitchen, deftly managing me, the dinner prep, and the children. "Do y'all want to have kids?" she asked.

"Eventually. We've only been married a year. We moved here so Ed could have his dream job at this tech start-up. There's too much going on career-wise to add kids to the mix," I had to stop talking because I didn't want my voice to quaver. The contrast was stark between Ed's work experience thus far in the South and mine. While he'd been caught up in his new job that paid more in stock options and less in cash, I'd run the gauntlet of interviews. Time and again, I was obstructed by the stereotypical ol' boys club barriers. Finally, I lucked into a job with a pre-IPO company.

"I applaud y'all for taking your time," JoDee said. "Live the life you want before you have kids, I say!" I silently agreed. Watching her intricate ballet of domestic duties only reinforced that I didn't yet want to be a parent. The guys rejoined us when JoDee yelled out the back door, "Supper's ready!"

After everyone washed up, we assembled at the dining room table. JoDee invited us to join in saying grace. Despite my discomfort with religious shows, I took Ed's hand in my left and Jay's in my right. As JoDee gave thanks, my mind wandered. I didn't want to be here, exposed. Fear gorged my neck. I didn't want to do this anymore! I needed to get home to my apartment, to hunker down in my bed, to hide. I clutched Ed's hand hard. JoDee finished the prayer.

"And most gracious thanks, O Lord, for bringing

Michelle and Ed home to us. They are welcome to our family! Amen." I burst into tears.

"Lord, have mercy!" JoDee jumped up and rushed to my side.

"I'm sorry," I wailed. Ed patted my hand but said nothing. This wasn't the first emotional outburst of mine he'd witnessed lately. "I don't know what's wrong with me," I wiped my nose on a tissue that JoDee handed to me.

"Hush, now," she soothed. "Everything's gonna be all right," she rubbed my shoulder while Ed peered anxiously into my face.

"I'm okay," I assured them. "Please, let's eat." JoDee stepped back and motioned for everyone to dig in. The baby whimpered, and dinner table noises covered my receding post-cry hiccups.

"Do you want to go home?" Ed whispered.

"No!" I grunted. How was I going to explain this to my dad and his wife? I looked like enough of a jerk already without adding a mid-meal exodus to the list of my offenses. JoDee observed our exchange.

"We're gonna talk about this after supper," she said. "Eat up, now. Y'all will feel better." I recalled Charlie's tip-off about her cousin's forceful personality. I was thankful that someone besides me was calling the shots. After we ate, the children were sent to play outdoors in the summer evening. JoDee insisted we leave the dishes for her to do later, then guided us to the comfy couches where she sat beside me.

"Tell me what's going on with you," she entreated, taking one of my hands in both of hers.

"Well, I have headaches," I told her, trying not to cry. "I'm kind of sad and tired all the time. I'm afraid to leave the apartment. Some days, I don't think I'll make it to work without turning back. Some days, once I get to work, I can't leave my desk because the hallway looks so long and there's nowhere to hide," my eyes swam up from our clasped hands to her face. "I can't sleep, and I can't stop thinking about *everything*," I felt stupid voicing these nonspecific complaints, but JoDee nodded.

"I know what you're feeling," she empathized. "You don't have to say another word."

"How do you know what I'm feeling?" I asked.

"Oh, honey," she chafed my forearm hard and half-laughed. "I've been there. I bet y'all already went to the doctor, didn't you? And I bet they didn't know what the problem was." She was right. I'd sought medical advice before we moved to North Carolina. Obsessive internet research fueled my budding hypochondria. Convinced I'd contracted AIDS, I appealed to our family physician. Dr. Roberts was about fifteen years older than me. He dismissed my concerns regarding HIV out-of-hand, telling me I had a case of the 'post-wedding blues' and should 'go get pregnant, give yourself something to do.' I left his office feeling deeply uneasy. I *knew* something was wrong with me, and making babies didn't seem like the way to fix it.

"Yes," I admitted to JoDee. "I went to our doctor in Denver. He told me I was bored, and I needed to get a hobby or start a family."

"Men!" JoDee scoffed hotly. "As if husbands aren't

bad enough, we have to deal with doctors who don't listen and don't understand," she looked over at her husband. "Ain't that right, Jay Bee?"

"That's right, darlin'," he answered on cue. It was impossible to tell if he agreed or was playing a supporting role for his leading lady.

"Do y'all have a doctor in Raleigh yet?" she turned back to me. I shook my head no. She dropped my hands and stood up. "Well, I'll be! I see the best women's doctor in the Triangle. Let me get his card for you." A moment later, she handed me a little cardboard rectangle and said, "Y'all visit Dr. Jack. He'll set you up with some antidepressant pills. You've got the blues, alright, just not the wedding blues. Everyone should take antidepressants, I swear." She laughed her breezy laugh and joked, "I might even petition the city council to add them to the water supply!"

MY MIND PARACHUTED back to Dr. Drexler's office, where I sat with Ed, fourteen years older, two kids later, on the opposite side of the country. How had I missed this? No thought of depression crossed my mind in all my long months of descent!

"Michelle," Dr. Drexler called my attention. "Listen to me. You have an illness, like the flu or heart disease. You need to address the symptoms and heal. I'm excusing you from work for two weeks due to medical disability."

"Thank you," I breathed. Two weeks excused from

work sounded positively luxurious! "I just need a little rest before I go back. This is perfect!" Dr. Drexler waited for me to finish.

"Let's not make plans to go back to work just yet," she cautioned.

"Oh, of course," I agreed. Dr. Drexler turned to Ed.

"Michelle needs to see a psychiatrist to manage her new prescriptions. One's for Celexa, an antidepressant. If she's not feeling better in a week, she should double the dose," Ed looked like a deer caught in headlights. Dr. Drexler saw it and said, "These instructions will be on her paperwork. I'm prescribing Klonopin for anxiety. Michelle should take Xanax when she feels acute distress, but take the Klonopin every day, even when she's feeling okay."

"Okay," Ed must've recovered from what spooked him because he sounded confident.

"I'm also ordering therapy twice a week," the doctor said. This was starting to sound like overkill. Between time off work and a return to Celexa, which was the same miracle drug prescribed by JoDee's doctor, I was sure I'd be fine. Dr. Drexler looked at me and said, "You'll come back for a two-week follow-up."

"Absolutely," I agreed, still on Cloud 9 over the work excuse.

"I'm serious," she continued. "When you come back, I'll ask you if you've already seen a psychiatrist and a therapist. If you haven't, you better have appointments teed up. If you don't, I will *personally* have you committed to a mental health program." It took a few seconds to process what she said. I looked at Ed, whose face was serene despite the almost-threat. "I know you, Michelle," Dr. Drexler recalled my attention. "You're an accomplished and determined Super Mom with a big career. You handle a lot more than the typical person, but what's happening to you is a warning sign. You need to get healthy, *now*."

"I understand," I promised. "I'll follow your instructions."

"I trust you will," she stood. "Bring me the names and numbers of whomever you plan to see because I'll confirm your appointments. See Violet on your way out. Take care of yourself," she hugged me and turned to shake Ed's hand. "Please help Michelle do these things," she requested.

"I will," he nodded.

AFTER ED and I finished at the front desk, we waited for the elevator holding hands. The euphoria over my extrication from work evaporated as we descended. What are the implications of taking two weeks off work for a mental illness, I wondered? Was I still going to be paid? We crossed the parking lot. Who would do my work while I was out? Ed and I arrived at my car door and dropped our handhold.

"Can you get the kids from camp?" he asked. "I had to reschedule a meeting when Dr. Drexler called. I should get back to take care of it." My brow darkened.

"Dr. Drexler said I need to rest," I began to reproach, but a pang of conscience over interrupting his work edged out my injured feelings. We were screwed if he lost his job again. "I guess I can get them today. You're going to have to step up and help me, though," I whined. "I can't handle all of this on my own!"

"I know, Shell. I heard Dr. Drexler," he checked his watch. "Getting the kids from camp is no more tiring than driving home, and you have to do that either way. I've gotta get this call done tonight, or I'll be holding up the rest of the team."

"Fine," I fired a verbal warning shot over his bow. "I guess I'll see you at home!"

"Shell, don't do this."

"Don't do what? I *said* I'd get them. What's your problem?"

"I'm going to help you," he insisted. "As soon as I take care of work."

CHAPTER 3

"*H*ello?" Monica said in my ear. "Michelle, is that you?" I stood on an island of debris-free floorspace in the office, my face wrenched in a grimace of silent tears. Ed surveilled me from another tiny island a few feet away.

"Give me the phone, please," he reached out. I flinched, stepping on some bubble wrap. "Please, Shell," he implored. "Let me talk to Monica." Unwilling to surrender, I tried to force words through my constricted throat.

"M-M-Monica, I—," was all I managed before my voice failed. Ed invaded my island and captured the phone from my clenched hand.

"Monica? Hi, this is Ed, Michelle's husband," he greeted.

"Is she okay? Has something happened?" Monica worried in the speaker next to Ed's face.

"Michelle's not feeling well," he said delicately. "She won't be in to work tomorrow," it was Sunday night.

My weekend memories were hazy. Driving the kids home Friday after the appointment with Dr. Drexler, anxiety seized me, and didn't let go. What if this is my fault, I wondered? I took all those pills, oodles of Oxy and Norco and Percocet. What if a psychiatrist puts two-and-two together? I raced on a hamster wheel of fear and indecision. The Ziplock remained stashed where I'd lobbed it after the miserable Independence Day party, despite my burning desire to medicate myself into oblivion. I tuned back into Ed & Monica's conversation.

"You heard her a minute ago," Ed said. "It's to the point where she can't talk."

"I'm sorry to hear all of this," Monica offered. "How long do you think she needs?"

"The doctor's excuse is for two weeks," Ed glanced furtively at me. "Michelle doesn't think she needs that much time. She wants to return to work next week."

"Do you think that's realistic?" Monica asked. Ed surveyed me more fully. I held my breath to suffocate my sobs. I hadn't showered in two days, and I was conscious that I smelled of back-to-school shopping, stale chlorine, and sweat.

"To be honest, I'm not sure," he admitted.

"I understand," Monica said. "Please fax the doctor's letter to our human resources department."

"Alright," Ed said.

"Will you please let me know how she's doing in a couple of days?" Monica asked.

"Sure thing," Ed hung up. He handed my phone to

me, saying, "You heard her, right?" I nodded. He picked his way from island-to-island to sit at his desk.

When it was clear he wasn't going to say more, I yelled, "Ed! What else did she say?" He swiveled around, surprised.

"Nothing. She just said she hopes you feel better, and send the letter to HR."

"What happens then?"

"I have no idea, Shell," he turned away. "Ask your HR department. I've never done this before."

"Well, neither have I!" I bit out. He rotated again.

"I know you haven't," he radiated the calm of a parent facing down a tempestuous toddler. "Tomorrow, you can call and find out. Meanwhile, take advantage of your time off. The kids are asleep. Go shower. Read in bed," I clung to every word, watching his familiar brown eyes. He added, "I'll be in after I finish work."

"I hope you'll come soon." I paused before adding, "I'm scared of the hand under the bed when I'm alone." This childhood fear of mine had alternately caused dissent and laughter between us over the years. "Even my blankee doesn't help anymore," I mourned. My ancient flannel baby blanket, stamped with faded yellow ducks frolicking on green patches of grass, still accompanied me to bed at age 39.

"There's no disembodied hand under our bed," Ed rushed to stave off my fear. "Just plastic containers covered with dust bunnies, full of too-small clothes," he waited for me to laugh. I didn't. He stood and hugged me. "I'll be in shortly."

. . .

27

I LEFT THE OFFICE, intending to follow his advice and take a hot shower. I hesitated at the junction where I would choose left to go to the bedroom or right to go to the garage. Over the weekend, Ed had unburied the tall ladder for gutter cleaning. It wasn't put away yet. The kids were quiet. I'd bet anything that Ed already had his noise-canceling headphones clamped over his ears. Like an observer at a tennis match, my head whipped right to left and back again.

I stepped toward the garage and jumped when a small voice rang out behind me, "Momma, where are you going?" Elsie materialized like an apparition.

With my hand pressed to my racing heart, I answered, "Nowhere, sugar."

"I can't fall asleep. Will you sing me a song?" I thought about the ladder, so close to my grasp. I *needed* that Ziplock. I'd been taking Celexa for three days, and nothing was getting better yet. It might be three weeks before I felt its effects if last time was any indicator. Eddie's bedroom door swept open.

"I can't sleep either, Mom," he announced.

"Fine," I knew the fastest way to get them back in their rooms was to comply. "I'll sing you a song. But only one! It's late, and you don't want to be tired on your first day of school." They scampered into Eddie's room, bickering over song choices.

"Quit arguing," I knelt at the edge of the bed, where they reclined side-by-side. "What song am I singing?"

"Rainbow Connection," they shouted in unison. Of course. It was the longest song I would consent to sing, and they knew it. I sang every word of all the verses; it was one of my favorites to play on the organ when I was little. After I finished, they begged for it again.

"Okay, okay," I surrendered. "Let me tuck Elsie in. I'll sing in the hallway." I carried Elsie to her bed, then stood between their doors to deliver the encore. I skipped a verse to hurry things up.

"No, Mom!" Eddie called out, while Elsie insisted, "Momma, sing it all!" I righted the wrong and accepted their ovation at the end of my concert.

"Good night, I love you," I said as I closed Elsie's door.

"Good night, Momma. I love you," she replied.

"Good night, I love you," I said as I closed Eddie's door.

"Mom, please leave it cracked," he whispered.

"Eddie," I sighed gustily. "You have to go to sleep now!"

"I will, Mom. I'm just scared of the dark."

"There's nothing to be afraid of, Eddie," I pushed back, unwilling to relinquish the Ziplock retrieval operation. "It's just the dark."

"I'm scared, Mom. Please," his plaintive whisper roused *my* fear of the dark.

"Okay, but you have to promise you won't get out of bed," I warned.

"I promise," his relief was palpable. "Good night, Mom. I love you." I closed the door most of the way and flipped the bird at the linen closet before stomping down the hall.

I pulled a gray plastic shower bench from the overstuffed closet in our bedroom. I carried it to the bathroom, where I swallowed an extra Xanax. I shucked off clothes, eyeing my nakedness in the mirror. The stark tan lines etched by the tropical sun looked like tribal markings. I made an angry tiki mask and shimmied my shoulders and hips. White, pendulous breasts and sagging mom-belly slapped from side-to-side like bread dough. I yanked open the shower door and sat down hard on the bench to welcome the inadequate numbness of Xanax.

Forty-five minutes later, I toweled off and put on shapeless thermal pajamas. I shivered. Ed must've set the thermostat to his preferred nighttime temperature, which approximated a blizzard at the North Pole. I slipped into bed, turned off the light, and tucked the comforter under my chin. A minute elapsed before I plucked up the nerve to sneak my hand out to grab my phone from the nightstand, quick as lightning. I didn't want to invite an encounter with the hand under the bed.

"It's freezing in here," I texted Ed. "What's the thermostat set to?"

"Sixty-three, same as always," he replied.

"I'm cold!" I sent.

"Turn on your heating pad," he suggested. In the dark, I made an angrier tiki mask. This tug-o-war was never mine to win. He'd claim he was sweating if I turned it up even two or three degrees, then turn it down to sixty in retaliation. Never mind that the electricity bill would top a thousand dollars again this month. Trying to shepherd my thoughts toward sleep, I wished Lydia was spooning me and playing with my nipples. My body grew warm with desire, but the fantasy stalled. I began to dream.

"Jay," my mom called from the edge of my consciousness. "Stop that. She's going to fall!" Strong hands gripped my ribcage. I was on a pony ride! I giggled, feeling secure with Daddy's arms around me. He wore wet swim trunks. The water from them seeped through the thin cotton skirt of the dress I'd worn to a neighbor's birthday party. My grubby feet, strapped in white leather sandals, dangled above aquamarine water.

My mom, visible now with hands on her hips, called to me this time, "Shelley, get down from there!" When we'd arrived home after the party, we'd found my dad swimming. He climbed out, sat on the diving board, and patted his lap to beckon me. I hesitated. The rule was that only one person at a time could stand on the diving board. Was he playing a trick on me? He bored his cornflower-blue eyes into my green ones. I hurried to comply, stepping onto the board. He twisted around to pull me into place. I was relieved I wasn't being yelled at. He started bouncing. That was when my mom objected. I could feel her frustration and fear, but Daddy and I were having fun!

"It's only water, Denise," he dismissed.

"We just bought those sandals! I don't want them ruined," she argued. I laughed, enjoying the turbulent ride. My dad loosened his grip, freeing me to bounce higher off his slippery legs. My mom moved toward us. The pool cleaner robot's tail broke the pool's surface and whipped a jet of water at her. I felt, rather than heard, my dad laugh when she jumped in surprise. Unfortunately, I also felt her jump with my empath sense. I flinched in unison.

My dad lost his grip on me.

I came down off-center on his lap before cartwheeling sideways into the water, where the pool cleaner robot lurked. I landed in a jackknife, my inner thigh slamming on the metal bar of its spine. I paddled and spluttered, blind with pain. My dad grabbed me under the arms and yanked me to safety. I was bawling.

"Goddamit, Denise," he yelled at my mom. "Why'd you interfere? Look what you did!"

"What *I did*?" she countered. "She's hurt, Jay! Give her to me," she reached for me, but my dad enclosed me tighter in his arms, both of us sopping wet. He looked down at me.

"What's wrong with you?" he asked in an accusatory tone.

"I landed on Agnes," I wailed. "She hurt my leg!"

"Why did you squirm?" he narrowed his eyes. "If you'd held still, you wouldn't have fallen," he set me down on uncooperative legs.

"Those sandals better not be ruined," my mom held out her hand for me to take. I put my hands behind my back and faced my parents.

"I didn't jump off," I asserted.

"Yes, you did," my dad corrected me.

"*I DID NOT!*" my roar echoed from the pre-cast

concrete fence encircling our backyard. "You dropped me on purpose," the accusation stopped my dad dead in his tracks. I felt my mom react, too. They moved in stereo, my dad stepping toward me menacingly and my mom slipping her hand onto the nape of my wet neck to pull me away from my dad.

I heard a man's voice call out, "Hey, neighbor, long time, no see!" The dad from next door, where my three friends lived, was staring into our yard. A slightly shorter version of my dad, he looked like a typical shirtsleeve-wearing 1970s engineer, complete with thick-rimmed photo-reactive glasses. I sent a silent thank-you his direction, relieved that he'd diverted attention from my insubordination.

"Hello, Edward," my dad turned, clearly wishing his neighbor long gone. As far as I could tell, my dad didn't like other men. The only friend he'd ever mentioned having was his best friend from high school, who also happened to be named Jay.

"Did I see you pushing a new Toro earlier?" Edward asked, eager to bond with my dad over the manly chore of lawn cutting. "That's the newest model, isn't it?"

"Yes, it is," I heard my dad's pained reply as my mom and I crossed onto the patio. She still gripped my neck.

"Take off your shoes," she let go. I handed the dripping footwear to her. "Take off that dress, too." I hesitated. The eyes of the next-door-neighbor dad darted from my dad's face as he bragged about the cost of his new machine to where my mom and I stood under the patio cover.

"I need a towel," I said.

"No one can see you," the neighbor-dad was out of her line-of-sight as she clipped my sandals to the clothesline. "Tsk," she clucked, contemplating them. "They better not be ruined," she looked at me. I was still wearing the wet party dress.

"I'm cold," I lied, desperate to keep my clothes on while he peered over the fence.

"Don't be ridiculous, Shelley. It's the middle of summer, and you're not going indoors with that on," she reached to pull it over my head. I sucked in my tummy, trying to make my body stiff and skinny as a pole so that I would be hidden from the neighbor's eyes.

I woke with a start just as my mom revealed my naked body. I recognized the dream; it was a long-buried memory of one of the many stand-offs that marred my parents' failed marriage. I stretched my fingertips to Ed's side of the bed, only to find it cold and empty. I wanted to text him, but the shadowy gulf at the edge of the mattress separated me from my phone. What if something grabbed my wrist when I reached out? The nightmare anxiety blew up.

"Don't touch me!" I shouted in the dark before darting my hand out. Nothing did. Still, I pulled the covers all the way over my head.

"I had a bad dream," I typed. "Where are you?" I paused, then deleted the first sentence. The memory of his reaction to my plane crash nightmare was still fresh.

"Working. Lost track of time," he replied.

"I can't sleep. I don't feel right," I crossed my fingers in the hope that he would come to check on me. I watched minutes tick past. Three minutes. Four. Five. I threw the heavy covers back and turned on the lamp in the same motion, minimizing my exposure to the dark. Eyes adjusting, I swung my feet over the bedside and judged it safe to set them on the floor. I padded through the house, flipping on every light switch.

"Hello?" I pushed open the office door. Ed's headphones were in place. He was absorbed in the three monitors that surrounded him, all displaying fast-moving text flying past as in a scene from *The Matrix*. I approached. He spun around when my shadow crossed his field of view.

"Hi, almost done," he smiled, pulling the headphones off.

"It's three a.m.!" I complained. "When are you coming to bed?"

"Five minutes," he made the familiar promise.

"Please, Ed," I implored. "Come to bed! I haven't been able to fall back asleep since—" my throat constricted. He glanced over his shoulder at the flashing text.

"I guess I can finish in the morning," he stretched, then stood to hug me. I sagged against him, fears receding. In the bedroom, he changed into bed shorts and brushed his teeth while I waited with the lamp on. I turned it out when he sat on his side. Almost as fast as

35

his head hit the pillow, he bounced up like a Weeble Wobble and said, "I forgot to send something."

"Can't it wait a few hours?"

"No, the client expects it in the morning," he stood up. "I'll be back in five minutes," he was out the door.

CHAPTER 4

*D*ays on leave blurred together in a barrage of panic attacks whose frequency and intensity accelerated. Some days, I what-iffed myself into a catatonic state. Other days, I tried to shake myself out of the unshakeable funk by ripping my fingers to shreds and digging into the raw cuticles. The exquisite, piercing pain was the only thing that dispelled the fog. The effect never lasted long, however. At least I could still take care of the kids with some semblance of normalcy; at any cost, I was determined to shield them from whatever was wrong with their mother.

When I arrived home from walking them to school one morning, I overheard Ed in the office.

"I don't know, Monica," he said. My heart, already thumping, sped up. "The doctor said it might be several weeks before the medications start working," he paused. "Her follow-up's in about a week. That's the soonest I can update you." He paused for longer, then said, "I wasn't aware that she logged in. I understand about the disability rules." My heart raced. My HR benefits coordinator had warned me not to work on leave! "I'll pass along the message. Thanks, bye."

"What was that about?" I demanded, bursting into the office.

"Jeez, Shell, you scared the crap out of me!" Ed jumped. Recovering from the startle, he said, "Don't you remember? I promised Monica I would update her. I left a message a couple days ago. She finally called back."

"Are they looking for an excuse to get rid of me? I'm sure Jay's thrilled I haven't been at work!"

"You only heard half the conversation," he shook his head in exasperation. "Monica's champing at the bit to get you back. She said not to worry because she and Troy have everything under control. Why'd you login, anyway?"

"To check my email! I have to stay on top of things."

"Shell, let Monica worry about it! You're supposed to be on leave, and disability insurance will deny your claim if you keep trying to work."

"They might as well deny it now," I moaned. "Do you realize, if I'm off longer than two weeks, my pay drops by half?" Ed looked nettled.

"We may have to figure out how that's going to work," he said. In my empath sense, I could feel the way he felt. It was like I used to feel, walking on eggshells around my dad when he was in a temper. "Why don't you go take a bath? We can tackle the money situation later."

"I'm *not* sending you a calendar invite!"

"I'm not asking you to," he was calm. "I'll do it for you."

I choked down a rude retort and said, "I can't take a bath! I haven't found a psychiatrist or a therapist." I'd made numerous calls to insurance and doctor's offices but was still without Dr. Drexler's required appointments. Ed's work phone rang.

"I have to get this," he said, checking the caller ID. "Taking one hour off from calling doctors is not going to make a difference. Go have a bath. Try to relax," he plunked an index finger onto the phone pad. "Hey, Tom," he greeted. "You ready to get started?"

I wandered out, Dr. Drexler's words nipping at my heels. I had no idea what it meant to be committed to a mental health program, and I didn't want to find out. I shut myself in the bedroom, opened the preferred providers list, and picked up calling where I'd left off the day before.

NIGHTS ON LEAVE CREPT PAST, my eyes burning with insomnia. The allure of the Ziplock grew more potent as the sleepless hours piled up. It was relocated to its former home beneath the bathroom sink. I'd completed Operation Ziplock Retrieval on the first day of school. Still, I was reluctant to make use of its contents. When I picked up the extra bottle of Celexa for the double dose, the pharmacist's questions set off a cascade of alarm bells.

"Is your doctor aware that you're taking several prescription painkillers?" he asked.

"Yes, of course," I wondered which ones were showing up.

"I see a couple strengths of the same medication," he traced a finger down his screen. "You don't take those simultaneously, do you?"

"Of course not," I snapped. "I'm not stupid!"

"This has nothing to do with stupidity," he looked dubious. "If you *accidentally* took one of each of these pills in close timing, you could die. You're overprescribed."

"I'm well aware of the dangers! My doctors and I have an ongoing dialogue," I didn't want to tell him I stopped taking the meds two months ago. What if he blocked future refills?

"Well, I can't imagine a responsible doctor approving of this," he pointed at the screen.

"Call Dr. Drexler and ask her, then," I dared without forethought. "Her number should be right there. Or I can give it to you," when I yanked out my cell phone, I felt his suspicions retract.

"That's not necessary," he yielded. Watching him staple white paper bags, I regretted my brazen gambit. What if he *did* reach out to Dr. Drexler? What if there was a blood test she could order that would reveal the drugs in my system? What if I took the painkillers and actually overdosed? The thought of my kids without their mom brought on the worst panic attack yet, leaving me nauseated and wide-eyed, unable to sleep

40

an entire night. But, I was deterred for the moment from self-medicating.

ONE NIGHT, I what-iffed for hours while Ed snored. Desperate to sleep, I stuffed down my fear of the hand under the bed long enough to make a dash for the bathroom. I flipped on the light and crouched in front of the cabinet.

"Shell, are you okay?" Ed called out, catching me with my hand in the cookie jar.

"I can't sleep," I called back with asperity.

"Your knee hurts?"

"Yes," I lied. "I'm taking ibuprofen."

"Can you bring me some?" Ed requested. "I have a headache." Eyes rolling, I withdrew my hand from under the sink to grasp the bottle on the counter. I made my way to his bedside. When he reached out a blind arm, I pressed the pills into his palm and handed him his water. "Thanks," he said, taking them without sitting up. In the bathroom, I swallowed five ibuprofen and kicked a knee petulantly against the cabinet door. Ed still clung to wakefulness when I climbed back in bed.

"Want to cuddle?" he offered. I didn't want his breath on my face, but I wanted to be close to him.

"Yeah," I scooped away the wall of pillows so I could slither over and snuggle against his side. It took forever to settle into a comfortable configuration. It seemed like wherever I lay, something of his was poking me, or something of mine was tickling him. Ten minutes later, as I drifted to sleep, Ed jostled me.

"I'm hot," he whispered. "Can we take the covers off?" There was no way, even cuddled against him, that I was going to sleep with my body uncovered in the dark. The hand might crawl up on the bed if it sensed my vulnerability.

"You can take them off of yourself," I said. "But I want mine on!" He tried to accommodate and ended up partially denuding me.

"Never mind," I sighed. "I can't fall asleep like this." I rolled away and rebuilt the wall.

"Sorry. Love you," he yawned.

"I love you," I said. His breathing evened out, and he started snoring. I wrapped my blankee twice around my neck to soothe me. Its soft touch against the sensitive skin at my throat stirred longing. I reached under the wall of pillows to shake Ed but stopped. It wasn't his touch that I craved. I turned my hand on myself. The ibuprofen must have numbed me because I couldn't feel my own seductive strokes, even when I thought about Lydia. I tucked my hand under my head, frustrated. What if the painkillers cemented my frigidity? What if I could never have another orgasm? The what-ifs escalated, putting sleep out of the question. I decided to sneak into the bathroom again. When I sat up, a new what-if entered my mind.

What if I hire a prostitute? Was there such a thing as a male prostitute to turn to, for suburban housewives in need or something? I shuddered. I didn't want to sleep with any other man besides Ed. All I wanted to know was, could I still have an orgasm?

What if I hire a female prostitute? This felt more probable to become a reality! Virtually all of my sexual fantasies centered around women. The full breasts, the warm musky scent, the whisker-less kisses that did not chafe my lips. Maybe my depression would dissipate if I sated this long-suppressed curiosity once and for all, I thought. I lay back, smiled in the dark, and fell deep asleep.

CHAPTER 5

*O*n the eve of my follow-up appointment with Dr. Drexler, Ed took the kids to the park while I watched over dinner cooking. After they disappeared down the street, I sat at my desk. I typed 'how do I hire a female lesbian prostitute' in the search bar. Cheeks burning, I hit enter and perused the results. After refining my search a few times, I discovered an ad for a women's escort service in San Francisco. I moused over it. Visions of another scene from *Office Space* played in my head. Three criminally clueless geeks, having committed embezzlement, were brainstorming how to launder the funds stolen from their employer. They resorted to looking up the definition of money laundering in a dictionary because they had no idea how to begin. Was this life imitating art, I wondered? I choked out a laugh.

"Shell?" Ed said behind me, causing me to jump clean out of my desk chair. I heard his voice approach, "What're you laughing at?"

I gasped, "That was a quick trip! I didn't expect you back so soon." I fumbled the mouse in my rush to close the incriminating window. I dove to the floor after it, mouth running a mile a minute to draw his attention. "I was thinking about that scene in *Office Space*, y'know, when they're trying to figure out how to launder money? It cracks me up!" Just as he crossed the halfway point of the room, I returned my mouse to the desk and closed the browser. With the same sweep of the pointer, I launched the screensaver, making a mental note to clear my history later. "Did you have fun at the park?"

In a doleful voice, Ed quoted the punchline from the movie scene: "What'm I gonna do with forty subscriptions to *Vibe*?" We laughed. "Were you trying to find a clip of that scene?" he asked. "I can rip it from the DVD if you want."

"No, thanks," I said, hoping he couldn't hear my heart race.

"Smells good," he sniffed. "Is dinner ready yet?"

"Should be about done," I herded him backward. "Let's go check!" The oven timer sounded.

"Wanna watch *Office Space* tonight after the kids go to bed?" Ed asked, finally turning to retreat.

"Sure," I kept herding. At that moment, I realized I was never going to have the nerve to go through with hiring an escort.

THE NEXT MORNING, I woke in a brighter mood than any day since the infamous work meeting. I'd had trouble sleeping, but not for the usual reasons. I'd lit on a thrilling new idea. It would require research and planning. In the meantime, I got the kids up.

"Good morning, sleepyhead," I crooned to Elsie.

"Momma," her eyelids struggled to part, "you sound happy today!" A shadow darkened my spirit. I'd have to work harder to shield her from my sadness. I tilted the blinds.

"I'm happy every day," I smiled like the sun streaming in. She looked unconvinced but allowed my white lie to go unremarked.

"Can I have cookies for breakfast?" she asked. I was torn. I didn't want to start the day saying no, but she'd put on weight lately. I was terrified of her following in my footsteps.

"No, I don't think so," Elsie heard the dilemma in my voice.

"Please, can I have just one?" she wheedled.

"Yes, okay, you can have one," I relented. "But none after school!" Beaming, she hopped up to dress. I moved to Eddie's room to repeat the wake-up process.

"Good morning!" I called. Unlike his sister, Eddie's eyes flew wide awake.

"Mom," he said, "I wanna play trains before I go to school today."

"There's no time, sweetheart," I said. "You need to get dressed and eat breakfast."

"I'm not hungry," he was already on the floor, dragging a train around the wooden track he'd left assembled the night before.

"Eddie," I warned, "stand up and put your clothes on." For a year, we'd been fiddling with his ADHD

46

medications, and this latest iteration did not bode well.

"I don't like school," he said, out of the blue.

"Why not?" My mind raced. He'd been on the receiving end of a bullying situation last year in third grade. What if it was starting again? "Are kids being mean to you?" I demanded.

"No, Mom, everyone's nice. It's just," he paused. "I wanna go to school with Ryder." Ryder had been Eddie's best friend since preschool.

"You can't go to the same school as Ryder," I explained for the thousandth time. "We live in a different neighborhood than the Baxters."

"Then why can't I be on the same baseball team as him?" Eddie's grievance called to mind our rift with Dan and Cathy and its subsequent fallout on the kids. Guilt of a different tenor than in Elsie's room washed over me.

I tried another approach, asking, "Do you like Mrs. Rambo?" I had a bad feeling about his teacher this year.

"Oh, I love Mrs. Rambo," he said staunchly. My empath sense felt a lie, but Eddie's look was earnest. "She helps me a lot," he nodded vigorously. I sighed. A more granular interrogation would have to wait; we were running out of time before the bell.

"If you get up and put your clothes on, you can have Pop-Tarts for breakfast," I bribed. Typically, they were reserved for special occasions, like when the parents slept in on the weekend.

"Okay, Mom," he accepted with a sunshiny smile.

I went to make a breakfast of cookies and Pop-Tarts.

. . .

WALKING home from escorting the kids to school, I noodled on my idea. I wanted to avoid a replay of the escort search debacle. I slowed my strides and let my mind wander back to the night I met Lydia after leaving her in the parking lot of the Hotel De Anza.

"MOMMY!" Eddie squealed, bouncing in Ed's arms. They'd been tossing a tiny football in the front yard, waiting for me to arrive home from my fictitious happy hour with colleagues.

"Hello, my two Eds," I kissed Ed on the cheek and tweaked Eddie's tummy through his purple football jersey. We headed indoors. I hung my jacket and briefcase on the hall tree before I turned to Ed. "I need to do something quick for work. Maybe you can start dinner?"

"We have a game on. We'll watch till you're done," he swung Eddie into a football hold that set off gales of toddler laughter.

"Alright," I turned toward the office and picked my way to my desk. From there, I watched them through the double doors that adjoined our office and family room. Ed whispered in Eddie's ear, pointing at the TV. I navigated to the dating site where I'd met Lydia. My cursor hovered over the 'delete my account' button. I sat there, second-guessing my decision. Eddie clapped and laughed. I redirected the cursor. My inbox held three new messages. One was from Lydia. Two were indications of interest from local women looking for a same-sex encounter. I deleted those before hesitating over Lydia's. I opened it.

"Hey, babydoll," it read, sending my eyeballs rolling. "I can't wait to put my tongue all over you. Email me so we can make plans while Ed is out of town," her email address followed. I ran my hands through my hair and thought about our date. Her fingers had been so light and teasing in the small of my back. But, the nicknames! Ick. It reminded me of awkward boys who crushed on me when I was young. My gaze fell on Ed, sitting companionably with our only child in the next room. I straightened my shoulders and hit delete. Lydia's message disappeared into the ether.

At the 'delete my account' page, indecisiveness struck again. I noticed a button I'd missed before.

"Click here to temporarily hide your account," it said alongside. When I moused over it, a pop-up read, "Your profile will no longer appear in search results. You may search personal ads, but you won't be able to initiate or respond to messages until you unhide your account."

"Shell?" Ed called from the next room. "You ready to start dinner? It's halftime." I clicked the button, figuring I'd sign on in a day or two to complete the process.

THE MEMORY FADED. I wiped my shearling boots on the doormat at home. The final school bell jangled in the distance, signifying it was time to put my plan into action. I pushed open the door.

"Ed?" I called. No answer. I went to find him. He wasn't working yet! I snuck down the hall and paused by the linen closet. He snored behind our bedroom door. I retreated to the office and shut myself in. I was prepared this time in case I had to cover my tracks when he opened the door.

I lost no time logging into my email.

I searched my inbox for Lydia's name. To my dismay, there were a few random results, all newer than three years. The time of my contact with Lydia was when Eddie was a toddler before Elsie was born. Way more than three years ago!

Sighing, I searched again, hoping to turn up an email from the dating website. The only results were old Yahoo! ads. Excitement overtook me. I remembered I used a secret email back then. I hadn't even thought of it for a couple years! I plodded through the password retrieval while my heart galloped.

I searched the secret email. At last, there it was; my old dating site login information! I paused. Ed's snores rattled through the lath-and-plaster walls of our early-1960s California ranch. I held my breath and clicked on the link. A totally different dating service's homepage appeared.

"Damn," I muttered, moving to close the browser. I stopped. What if the old login still works, I wondered? I guessed at a password. The screen loaded.

"Invalid password. Click to reset." I started to follow the steps, but excitement liquefied my bowels. I ran for the bathroom. Just as I made it to the toilet, my phone rang.

It was my mom.

I didn't want to answer, but I knew if I didn't, she'd call and text till I responded.

"Hello," I answered. "I'm pooping, so be forewarned."

"Hi, honey. Why haven't you called me?" she asked, disregarding my veiled request for privacy.

"I've been busy," I griped. "We have lots going on!" As far as my mom knew, I'd been granted permission to work from home for a couple weeks. "I can't talk. I have work."

"Well, I never know when's a good time to call," she complained. "You're always so busy! I wait for you to call me, but you never do."

"Mom, I'm sorry," I whined. "We barely get through everything we need to in a day, between work and school! And now flag football is starting."

"But your mom wants to talk to you," she insisted. "We need to arrange our travel plans. You're not the only kids we have, you know! Others are waiting on your decision because you get first choice." As usual, my mom and Matt were planning a winter holiday road trip that would encompass a visit to our house as well as to at least one of my stepbrothers' homes. She'd been pressing me since their summer visit to choose which week I preferred.

"Mom, I don't know!" I seethed. "Ed hasn't told me

what week he can take off. You're gonna have to wait," a little shot of adrenaline quickened my tongue. "Or, don't see us this year. It isn't like you've never been here at Christmas."

"We always spend Christmas with you! Why don't you want us to come?" I could hear the hurt I'd triggered. Guilt and glee flooded me.

"That's not what I said."

"Well, that's what it sounded like, Shelley! You know, we aren't going to be around forever," I tuned her out and reconnected to my earlier memory, picking up a week or so after I hid my old dating site account.

ED WENT to bed early that night. My attention wandered from the presentation I was trying to finish. I was horny all the time since I stopped taking birth control pills; Ed and I were going for baby number two. I longed to sip wine with Lydia and kiss her again! Her smoky voice and soft fingers haunted me.

I shook my head to clear the fantasy. In its place, I replayed the intervention scene from *But I'm a Cheerleader*. The main character's parents and friends pushed her to enter a conversion therapy camp to cure her lesbianism. It didn't work.

I loaded up the dating site and unhid my account.

The inbox contained ten emails from Lydia. A warning sounded in the back of my head. I opened the oldest one first, from the morning after our De Anza date.

"Hey, babydoll," it said. "I saw you read my message last night," I smacked my forehead. She would see the read notification for these messages now, too! "I know you were tired and had to feed the boys," it continued. "Email me when you get a chance."

I clicked to the next one, stamped twelve hours later.

"I'm getting concerned," it said. "I searched for your profile so I could look at your beautiful pic, and it's gone!" Uh-oh, I thought. "Looks like you haven't read the message I sent earlier. I'll check in tomorrow. Sleep well, babydoll."

Click. This one was sent before six a.m. the following day.

"I suspect you're avoiding me. It's been two days! I thought we were going to make plans for when Ed's away? I hope you're okay." My intuition whispered to delete the rest.

Click. Only two hours later.

"I know you're ditching me," it began. "I didn't think you were that kind of person. So many women have done this to me. It shouldn't surprise me. Good luck. I hope you find what you're looking for." I cringed, feeling the well-placed criticism.

Click. A whole day had elapsed.

"I'm sorry," went the one-sided conversation. "I talked to Bill. He says it's unlikely you're avoiding me. He says I should give you some space because you're probably busy. I hope that's true. Please accept my apology for the rude message."

Click. Afternoon, same day.

"Hi, there! Checking on my babydoll," I crinkled my nose.

Click. Evening, same day.

"I had a terrible day at work. I gave performance reviews to my team. The reviews were not complimentary because they need to shape up! Someone complained to my boss. Civilians never respect the chain-of-command," she lamented. "And they're a bunch of sissies. I wish I could vent to you over a glass of wine."

Trapped in a slow-motion train wreck, I clicked again.

"I know your profile is hidden. I tested with a fake account. So, I guess you're getting my messages and ignoring them. I don't know what I did wrong, but I'm sorry." Now I felt like a jerk for leading her on.

Click. From yesterday.

"Just checking."

Click. This morning.

"I had to check one last time. I'm taking off work today. I can't concentrate. Good-bye." I paused to let it all sink in. A chat request popped up. It was from Lydia. I hit 'accept' and started typing.

"Hey, sorry I've been MIA! Work's been insane," I hit enter.

Her message appeared: "Why are you ignoring me?"

"Why would I ignore you?" I typed. "When I'm busy at work, I need to eliminate distractions." I decided to lay it on thick, "In any case, why would I be on the dating site now that I met you?" She sent a silly kitten sticker with hearts pasted over its eyes.

"Want to get together while Ed's gone?" she sent. "Bill would like to make dinner over here so you can meet him and our son." I took a deep breath.

"I'm up late working. Can I message you tomorrow?"

"Do you still have my email?" she sent back.

"Yes," I typed. "Gotta go."

"Hugs and kisses," she sent.

I closed out of the chat window and shut down my computer.

"SHELL? ARE YOU THERE?" my mom's voice broke through the reverie. My butt was molded to the toilet seat. I must have missed the end of her lecture.

"Yes, I'm here," I sighed, wiping. "I have to go. I have an appointment with Dr. Drexler."

"Oh? What for?" she asked.

"Just a follow-up," I evaded and flushed. "I'll talk to Ed when he wakes up. We'll nail down Christmas dates for you."

"Why's Ed still asleep?" she asked as I walked on pins and needles back to the office. "Doesn't he have to work? It worries me that he sleeps so much."

"He had a late deadline last night," I covered for him to hurry things along.

"Okay. Tell him I love him, and the kids, too."

"I will. Bye, Mom," I sat in front of my screen saver.

"Oh, wait," she called. "Do the kids like their teachers this year? How's school going?"

"Mom, I have to go! We'll talk about it later."

"Alright, fine," she sounded miffed. "When are you going to call me?"

"I don't know, when I have time to, I guess!" I heard the office door open behind me.

"Who're you yelling at?" Ed asked while my mom's voice buzzed in my ear, "I'm your mother, Michelle, and I want to hear from my only daughter!" Ed answered his own question, saying, "Oh, it's your mom. Tell her to call me on my phone, so I can walk her through fixing her laptop."

Something in me snapped.

"Everyone, leave me the fuck alone!" The shout tore through my mouth, roughening my throat and setting stars dancing in my vision.

"Whoa, Shell, it's okay," Ed started toward me with his palms pressed forward while my mom grumbled, "You don't have to yell, Michelle. I know you have work to do."

"Goodbye, Mother," I managed to say into the phone.

"Call me back soon," she hung up. Ed leaned against the edge of my desk to peer into my face.

"Shell, are you okay?" he asked.

"Yes," I said.

"What'd your mom want?"

In a toneless voice, I answered, "To know which week they should come during winter break."

"Oh, right. I'll check the team calendar today and let you know."

"Fine," I stared unblinkingly at him.

"Did you tell her about leave?" he asked.

"No."

"You're acting like an automaton again," he started to look more concerned.

Knowing it would draw his attention off of my odd behavior, I said, "I need to eat something."

"Me, too! Wanna go to Panera?" he asked. I nodded. He pushed off the desk and said, "Back in a sec and we can go."

While he changed, I moved my mouse to wake my computer. There was nothing in the inbox or trash of my recovered dating site account. Hopes dashed, I closed everything and cleared my browser history.

CHAPTER 6

"*W*here's Ed today?" Dr. Drexler asked as she peeled the blood pressure cuff off my arm.

"Ed had a work call he couldn't miss," I said. The truth was, I'd found out at Panera that he scheduled a meeting over my appointment despite my sending him a calendar invite.

"Mmm-hmm," Dr. Drexler murmured. She recorded my vitals. My lips parted to make excuses, but she spoke first. "You know, after I had my daughter, it became clear that my family was not going to fit the framework of the modern dual-income household," she sat on her stool. "My husband and I were spread too thin. We had a newborn, and then our son got diagnosed with autism—" her anecdote triggered my worries over Eddie.

"Eddie told me he doesn't like school," I blurted. "What if his ADHD is getting worse?"

"He might need extra help as he grows up," Dr.

Drexler was patient with my interruption. "But I'm sure he's going to be fine."

"I know, it's just—" I bit down on what I wanted to say.

"Just what?" Dr. Drexler asked, studying me over her glasses like a pale, blonde owl.

"Is *this* genetic?" I waved my hands around my head.

"Depression and anxiety run in families if that's what you want to know," she said. "I've seen ADHD and autism transmit in my own."

"What d'you mean?" I asked, surprised.

"It's never been confirmed by another doctor, but I know my husband is on the autism scale. He also has adult ADD. They're the same diagnoses as our son, and the similarities between the two of them are uncanny." My thoughts turned to my husband and son.

"Eddie's a lot like his dad," I tried to feel into the best way to broach a request.

"Yes, I've noticed," the doctor said. Despite her neutral tone, I was defensive.

"I don't think he can help it," I said. "Especially when I hear stories from my mother-in-law about Ed when he was little!"

"I *know* he can't help it," she confirmed. "However, it *is* something that can be helped with the right medications, which is why you're working with Eddie's psychiatrist. Don't worry, Michelle, you're doing all the right things."

"Do you mind my asking, does your husband take medication for his condition?"

"He takes some of the same medications as Eddie."

"Do they help?" I asked.

"Yes. He also goes to counseling, and he's done behavior modification training."

I chewed my lip a moment then proceeded with my request; "Could you write a referral for Ed to see someone who can diagnose him with adult ADD?" She looked taken aback, so I rushed to explain. "Ever since I filled out all those surveys for Eddie's ADHD diagnosis last year, I haven't been able to get it out of my head that he and Ed have a lot of the same…behaviors."

Dr. Drexler nodded and said, "Why don't you speak to Ed when you go home? Suggest that he see me, and I'll talk to him about his options."

"Alright," I sighed. If Ed had to drag himself to an appointment with Dr. Drexler, I was prepared to be disappointed.

"Okay, let's talk about you. After all, this is *your* appointment, not Ed's or Eddie's." I squirmed. "How're you doing with the Celexa?" she asked.

"I doubled it like you instructed. I don't think it's helping."

"What about the Klonopin? Is your anxiety responding?"

"I think so," I was bullish on the Klonopin. When I took extra on an empty stomach with ibuprofen, I felt a shadow of the old opioid bliss. "I've needed several Xanax per day, though," I admitted. "The panic attacks are worse and more often." On cue, worry sprung up inside my chest. "Why am I not getting better yet?" I implored. "What if the drugs never work? Last time I didn't have to take anti-anxiety meds!"

"It can be several weeks before antidepressants build up enough in your system to make a difference in how you feel," she explained what I already knew. "So, we're not going to change that today. We can probably increase your Xanax, though," she peered at her computer. "Oh, yes. You'd have to take eight of your current ones to achieve the maximum dose in a day. I'll write a script for bigger pills." I wondered how many it would take for me to descend into a deep, dreamless slumber for eight hours.

"Is there anything you can give me to help with insomnia?" I asked. "I can't sleep, and when I do manage to fall asleep, nightmares wake me up."

"Have you tried Tylenol PM? I hesitate to prescribe anything because some sleep drugs can worsen anxiety."

I slumped and said, "Alright."

"I know, insomnia is awful," Dr. Drexler commiserated. "I struggled with it for years. Make sure you talk to your psychiatrist. They'll know what to prescribe," she said. "Speaking of which, were you able to make appointments?"

"Yes," I fished in my purse. I handed her a note with names, numbers, dates, and times.

"Oh," she exclaimed. "Your first appointment with a therapist is today?" I nodded. "You're lucky! It's rare to find an opening so quickly."

"Tell me about it," I griped.

Stealing a glance at the clock, Dr. Drexler said, "Let's

move on to the disability extension letter for your manager."

"What extension?" I was caught off-guard. "I have to go back to work Monday!"

"Michelle, you're not going back to work yet," she spoke slowly. "You haven't seen the psychiatrist or psychologist, right?"

"You know I haven't," I snapped. "But I got the appointments like you said to!" Full-blown panic ensued, and I started babbling, "I can't do this, Dr. D. I'm going to lose it! And, if I do, it's all over. I have to go back to work while I still can! I'm like the little Dutch boy with his fingers plugging the holes of the dike," I jumped up, fingers splayed, jabbing the air. "Do you understand?" I supplicated wildly.

"Michelle, you're okay," Dr. Drexler approached cautiously and reached for my shoulder. "*This* is exactly why I will not clear you to return to work."

"I have to go back, even if it kills me!" I clenched my fists in a boxing stance to ward her off.

"Please sit," she invited gently. I flopped face-first onto the exam table and howled. The doctor patted my back, like my mom used to when I had trouble sleeping. I eventually fell quiet. She said, "Can you listen now?"

"Yes," I whispered.

"Good. You are *not well*. Staying home to take care of yourself is not a weakness—" I laughed, loud and bitter.

"We can't make it without my paycheck," I moaned into the table.

"Michelle, that's gonna be the least of your worries,"

she warned, sparking a vicious round of the what-if game. It ended with, what if this is genetic like she says? What if I end up like my aunt? At the thought of Juliet, the what-ifs went nuclear. I felt the automaton mask settle.

"Okay," I pushed myself upright. Dr. D backed away and eyed me.

"I'm glad you're going straight to the therapist from here," she sat down at her computer.

"What am I supposed to do all day when I'm not at work?" I asked in a wooden voice.

"What do you like to do outside of work now?" Dr. Drexler asked, starting to type.

"I guess I like to knit," I shrugged.

"Well, maybe you can find a knitting group at the community center," she suggested. Pausing to reread, she added, "I saw HeartMath and Reiki classes in the Parks & Rec catalog."

"What're they?" I asked.

"HeartMath would help you *and* your family, especially your kids," she said. "It teaches coping skills and stress reduction. My whole family uses it."

"What's the other?" I couldn't remember the word.

"Reiki," she said tentatively, typing some more. "I'm not sure how to pronounce it. Stanford started using it recently on cancer patients."

"Maybe I can look into that," I said without much hope or intention of following through. She finished typing and looked up at me.

"I'm authorizing another two-week absence from work. I want you to promise you'll take off another month after. Your psychiatrist can fill out the continuance paperwork."

"A whole month *more?*" I squeaked.

"Yes," she said. Under the light tone, I felt her unbending will.

"Okay," I waved the white flag.

"Thank you," Dr. Drexler said. "I'll be back after I grab your paperwork."

THE SLUGGISH DUST devil of what-ifs twirled in my mind as I drove south, toward Mission San Jose, to find my therapist's office. Tired of their repetitive loops, I centered my thoughts on Lydia. Inside an old adobe office building up the street from the mission, I settled to wait in a common area that served a pod of five therapists. White noise machines whirred at each of their doors.

I was twenty minutes early, and the little sign on Dr. Julia Brewer's door was turned to read, 'The doctor is out,' just like Lucy's in the Peanuts comic strip. The white noise lulled me straight into a daydream.

"I'M REALLY ENJOYING MYSELF," Lydia rasped. The wine perfume on her breath triggered déjà vu, causing the Lydia on our family room couch to merge into the Lydia of the red hotel lobby couch. With a pang of longing, I wished she'd ask to see my tattoo again. She gazed into her lap and said, "Can I see your tattoo again?" Tipsy and shocked by the speed with which my wish was granted, it took a minute to reply.

"Yes," I croaked and cleared my throat. "How about some more wine first?"

"Sure," she looked up, emboldened by my acquiescence. Her next words were commanding, "I want to see your other tattoo. The one you wouldn't show me at the hotel."

"Maybe, maybe not," I flirted, snagging the empty wine bottle by its neck and waggling it at her. "Lemme replace this bottle. Then we can negotiate." She groaned and crossed her arms.

On my way back from the kitchen, Eddie met me in the hall. I was startled and dropped the new bottle of wine. Thankfully, instead of hitting the foyer's tile edge, it landed on the wool area rug and bounced without breaking.

"Eddie," in my nervous fright, I spoke harshly. "Why are you out of bed?"

"I'm sorry, Mommy," he toed the rug. "Who were you talking to?" I darted my eyes toward the dimly-lit family room.

"No one," I said.

"I heard you talking. Was it Daddy on the phone?" he asked.

Thankful for the ready-made excuse, I said, "Yes, sweetheart. Now go back to bed." I bent to retrieve the wine bottle.

"I wanna talk to Daddy," Eddie said hopefully. My eyes skimmed over his two-year-old face. I rose, bottle in hand. Like any small boy, Eddie idolized his father. I felt how much he missed Ed.

"Okay, Eddie, we can do that," I sighed. "Go turn on your bedroom light, and I'll bring my phone." He skipped down the hall, leaving me to determine whether I was more relieved or more irked at the interruption. What if Eddie wandered out and witnessed Lydia in our family room? Or worse, found me and Lydia buck naked, locked in lesbian passion? I shuddered.

"Michelle?" Lydia's voice approached from the family room. As she rounded the corner into the foyer, she demanded, "Where'd you go?" My hand flew up to caution her into silence. I checked Eddie's door. I doubted he heard her over the scraping of toys across his floor. I motioned for her to follow me back to the family room. She grasped my free hand as I passed; the gesture cemented my unwillingness to carry on. I turned on my heel and dropped her hand. It stuck to mine briefly, then peeled away like a wacky wall-walker.

"I can't do this tonight, Lydia," I was careful to filter the relief out of my voice. "Eddie woke up. He wants to talk to Ed on the phone." Lydia looked crestfallen. "I'm sorry," I continued, "but when Eddie wakes up and Ed's on a trip, it's impossible to get him back to sleep."

With a skeptical look, she said, "He won't go back to sleep *all night?* Because I could go in your bedroom and wait for you to get him back to sleep. It isn't like Bill expects me home tonight!"

"No, I'm sorry," I shut her down. "Ed wouldn't be

comfortable if he found out a stranger was in our house."

"You told me Ed knows about our seeing each other," Lydia said. "So, I'm not exactly a stranger," she paused. "He *does* know, doesn't he?" I cursed myself for choosing careless words. Ed most certainly did *not* know about my dalliance with Lydia, and I never intended to tell him.

"Yes, of course, he knows," I said in an airy voice. "I just didn't tell him you were coming here *tonight*. He asks for all the details when we see each other, and I wasn't sure I'd want to share with him," I peppered the lies with flirtation.

"Oh, I get that," she was quick to forgive. "Bill always wants the blow-by-blow when I'm with another woman. Every gruesome detail! Typical male," she laughed.

"Why don't you get your things together?" I tried to hurry her. "I'll meet you by the front door." I tiptoed to Eddie's room and peeked around the corner. He was as I expected, playing on his floor with dinosaur figures. I calculated that I had a good fifteen minutes before he came hunting for me. I tiptoed back to Lydia, who waited in the foyer with her coat on.

"I rinsed the wine glasses and left them by the kitchen sink, babydoll," she said softly. I donned a sweater from the hall tree. "I'm looking forward to next time," she moved in to embrace me. I stiffened and sneaked a glance at the hallway.

"Let me walk you out to the car," I offered. Backing away, Lydia smiled wistfully.

"Aw, we'll have to save it up," she sighed. "Maybe next time, Ed can watch Eddie while you and I get a hotel room." Irritated, I yanked open the door to step into the fog that rolled off the bay. She followed. I stopped in the driveway between our cars to face her. She reached for me, and I allowed her to weave her fingers together with mine. Like a perverse pendulum, my horniness and curiosity peaked again. Lydia dragged me toward her. Our lips hovered close, exchanging warmth but not meeting. My phone shrilled. I jerked, abandoning the impending kiss and ripping my hands out of Lydia's.

"It's Ed," I whispered after I wrestled the phone from my pocket. Lydia hissed. Shocked at the sound, I stared at her. Her hazel-brown eyes pleaded with me to ignore the call. I hit answer.

"Hey! How was the dinner?"

"Good. It ran late. How're you and Eddie doing?" Ed yawned.

"We're fine. In fact, Eddie woke up a little while ago and wants to—"

Ed interrupted to ask, "Why does it sound like you're outside?"

"I'm looking at the moon. Someone posted about it on Facebook," I was still staring at Lydia, who was watching me lie fluidly to my husband.

"Isn't it foggy there?" he asked. I hated being pinned between them!

I kept my cool and answered, "It's still too windy for the fog to settle."

"Oh, okay. Well, I'm heading to bed. Got an early start tomorrow morning," he yawned again.

"What about Eddie?" I interposed. "He's awake, and he wants to talk to you."

"What's he doing up at this time?"

"I told you, he woke up and wanted to talk to you. Are you going to talk to him or not?" I shivered in the damp under Lydia's stare.

"I'll call him tomorrow morning when you're getting ready for daycare," Ed bargained.

"Ed, he's not going back to sleep till he talks to you," I argued.

"Shell, I'm exhausted," he moaned.

I snapped, "Fine! Talk to you tomorrow. Good night," I hung up. Lydia still watched me.

"Everything alright?" she asked.

"I have to go in and deal with Eddie," I grumbled.

"I can't imagine traveling and not wanting to talk to my son every chance I got," she commented. Her voice dropped an octave to add, "I'd want to talk to *you* all the time, too." I sensed the lust flaring in her. I shivered and crossed my arms.

"I've gotta go in, Lydia," it was time to find Eddie. "Thanks for coming over. I'm sorry things didn't work out."

"There's always next time," she said, reaching out to slip her hand behind my neck. She pulled me forward for a quick peck on the lips. "Good night, babydoll. I'll message you when I get home," she ducked into her car and drove off. I retraced my path to Eddie's room. He was engrossed in the dinosaurs.

"Time for bed," I announced. He looked up.

"No, Mommy," he tested me.

"Eddie," I warned, "you have school in the morning. And, remember, you want to go to Ryder's party this weekend. If you don't go to bed, you can't go to Ryder's party." He hopped to his feet.

"Okay, Mommy. I'll sleep!" I tucked him in, relieved he'd forgotten Ed.

I headed for the kitchen, where I scooped up the abandoned wine bottle. Perched at my desk clutching a full glass, I deleted my account on the dating site. I took a deep swig before loading up first one email account and then the other. From them, I erased every message Lydia and I had exchanged. I turned my computer off.

Toting the wine, I relocated to the abandoned family room. I sat on the couch in Lydia's spot to watch, *But I'm a Cheerleader*. I replayed the big sex scene five times while I killed the bottle. I never heard from Lydia again.

"Michelle?" a mousy-haired woman of about sixty stood before me. "Hello? Are you Michelle?" I emerged from the daydream into a river of white noise.

"Yes, sorry, I was somewhere else," I excused myself. "Are you Dr. Brewer?"

"I'll say you were somewhere else! Pleased to meet you. Call me Julia," she stuck out her hand. We shook, then she gestured to the door where the sign had been turned to read, 'The doctor is in.' Julia raised her eyebrows and asked, "Are you ready?" I preceded her into a small office.

Eyeing an oatmeal plaid sofa dotted with colorful pillows, I asked, "How does this work? I've only seen therapists on TV and in movies. Do I have to lie down?"

She chortled and said, "Only if you want to! Make yourself comfortable." I sat primly on one cushion at the end of the sofa. Julia passed me a clipboard holding a sheaf of paper and a blue ballpoint pen. "I'll be back in a few minutes," she closed the door behind her. I stared at the forms. The clipboard swelled in my grip, its weight bearing down on my arm. It took every ounce of my self-control to print answers in the parade of tiny boxes.

"All set?" Julia reappeared. I nodded. We went over my answers. Finally, she shuffled the papers away into a manila folder and checked her watch. Settling back with a black leather-bound notebook in her lap, she said, "We have a handful of minutes left. Why don't you tell me more about why you're here? It'll give us somewhere to start next session."

"There's a lot of mental illness in my family that worries me," I was relieved to say it out loud.

"Who and what type of mental illness?" Julia turned to a new page in her notebook.

"Well, my mom was diagnosed with depression after my parents divorced," I began. "And her sister suffers from schizophrenia and paranoia. I'm positive that their brother, my uncle, had some kind of mental illness. He died about five years ago. But he was never diagnosed, as far as I know," past the initial hurdle, my words picked up speed. "My mom's dad, when I look back on my memories of him, I know he was depressed. On my dad's side," my voice trailed off. This was a more challenging admission to make. "My uncle killed himself when I was six or seven. At least, that's what I remember some of the adults saying at his funeral." I waited for Julia to finish note-taking.

"Is that all?" she asked. I nodded. Julia wrote some more. The white noise seeping under the door was too quiet to cover up the scratching of her pen. Neither did it obscure the ticking of the clock on her desk. Time stretched like taffy.

"What if this is genetic?" I burst out, causing Julia to jump. "I'm going to end up just like my aunt. I know it!"

She put down her pen and said, "I know it's hard to believe this right now, but you're gonna be okay."

"It doesn't feel like it," I moaned.

"I promise, you're going to be okay," she reiterated. "What you're feeling are normal emotions that've grown a little out-of-control. You're here to learn how to prune them back and keep them orderly."

"But these are serious mental illnesses," I argued. "My regular doctor told me right before I came here that mental illness runs in families!" Julia closed her notebook.

"Mental illness can show up in successive generations. However, you don't have schizophrenia. You don't have paranoid delusions. You are anxious and depressed. And we're going to get the better of it," she smiled. "Time's up. How's Tuesday for our next session?"

"Fine," I yawned. Over an hour had passed since my daydream in the waiting area. I hungered for something to smooth the rough edges of this long day. Julia and I exchanged goodbyes.

Buckling into the driver's seat, my thoughts alighted on Lydia again. What if she no longer lived nearby? What if she was currently in a relationship with a woman, or her understanding with Bill had changed? Deeper down the rabbit hole, I fell. I wondered if she would like me with red hair. Right now, my hair was exactly the same as when we'd said goodbye in the driveway.

Something dawned on me. I didn't remember Lydia's last name.

"What's her last name?" I squinted in the rearview mirror. "What's her last name?" I repeated. The question lodged itself, like an earworm, in my mind. It played on repeat through dinner and family movie night. When I climbed in bed and sleep proved elusive, I pummeled my brain with the question so intently that I forgot to lust after the Ziplock bag.

CHAPTER 7

Sitting under the salon dryer a week later, I remembered.

"Gorman!" I exclaimed. Everyone looked to see who yelled. "Sorry, sorry," I apologized too loud, unable to gauge my volume through the rustling foils that my stylist had woven into my chestnut locks. "I just remembered something I've been trying to remember forever!" Smiling forgiveness, everyone turned away.

A warm glow enveloped me. Since meeting Julia, I'd spent days googling and perusing the Facebook profiles of dozens of Lydias. My Lydia remained stubbornly concealed. When insomnia struck, I used the interminable hours to scheme how I'd do things differently this time. Because, as the days passed, my certainty grew that our paths were destined to cross again. Just as I willed her to ask to see my tattoo a second time all those years ago, I intended to will her presence back into my life. I grinned like a Cheshire cat. Trina, my stylist, approached to check my hair process.

"That's a good look on you," she commented, pulling on my scalp as she pried open a couple of the foils. I winced. Ed and I drank too much the night before. Copious amounts of tequila, coupled with two of the big Xanax tablets at bedtime, resulted in ten hours of uninterrupted sleep for the first time in what felt like a decade. I woke still drunk, however, and was paying the price. Trina rendered her verdict, "You need a little longer to finish." She patted the foils back in place and drew the bonnet over my head.

"How much longer?" I asked. "I have a Zumba class at two."

"I'll do my best, but you can't rush art," she apprised, tapping her watch and setting a dozen bead bracelets clicking. Panic prickled but did not overwhelm me. I couldn't miss this class! As the dryer picked up velocity, Dr. Basu's austere countenance floated in my vision, and I recalled our first meeting.

"WHAT ARE you doing to help yourself feel better?" she asked in a no-nonsense tone after I labored for forty-five minutes to explain my situation.

I dabbed at raw eyelids with a limp tissue and asked, "What do you mean?"

"How are you taking care of yourself?" she rephrased. Ticking on her fingers, she said, "You needn't worry about work right now. Your children are in school all week. Your husband is a grown person. All you must do is care for yourself." She spread her hands wide when she finished counting off my responsibilities. "How are you doing that?"

"Well, I'm taking my medications and trying to sleep at night," I felt defensive. "Dr. Drexler suggested signing up for classes at the community center, so I'm looking into that. What else am I supposed to be doing?" I watched her give me an exaggerated once-over.

"You are not in a healthy place," she pronounced. "Your mind cannot be healthy if your body is not healthy."

"I've only been on leave for a couple weeks!" I deflected. "I'm gonna start running again when I get cleared by my orthopedic surgeon." Dr. Basu looked nonplussed.

"When do you see your surgeon?" she inquired.

"Next month," I lied. I was too embarrassed, after skipping two appointments, to reschedule with Dr. Holliday a third time.

"Psychiatric drugs alone will not heal you. Your mind will be clearer if you get fresh air and exercise for your body, and feed it healthy foods," she was emphatic. "What physical activity is currently allowed by your surgeon?"

"I'm still going to physical therapy," I said, stung. "That's a weightlifting workout twice a week!"

She answered herself, "You can walk. I want you to walk three times, for one hour each time, before you see me again. Is this something you can do?"

"Yes, I suppose so," I sulked.

"We will discuss your progress when we meet again,

including medications. Not enough time has passed on your current doses." She made a note in my chart and added, "You must take fewer Xanax." I damned myself for being honest about my consumption.

"How'm I supposed to sleep?" I whined. "I've barely slept in months!"

Dr. Basu kept her eyes on my chart and said, "If you exercise more, you will sleep." Lead filled my stomach.

"Isn't there a sleeping pill you could prescribe?" I asked hopefully.

"We shall assess medications next visit," she stood to usher me out of her office.

In the parking lot, I started the engine. The lead in my stomach dragged me down. The chaos of what-ifs filled my head. Minutes passed while I stared without seeing.

"Snap out of it," I yelled, banging my fist on the steering wheel. "You don't have a choice!" I was trapped with Dr. Basu. It'd been harder to find a psychiatrist than to find a therapist.

My phone dinged, announcing a text from my friend Genevieve. Genevieve was an active woman with a megawatt smile, and one of the only friends with whom I'd shared the news of my illness. "Wanna walk tomorrow morning at Ohlone?" the text read.

"YES," I sent back. At least I'd be able to rub Dr. Basu's nose in one walk when I returned.

THE DRYER BUZZED in my ear, recalling me to the salon. Trina pronounced my hair ready to wash. As she lathered, rinsed, and chatted with her fellow stylists, I went back to thinking about all that transpired since I met Dr. Basu.

THE FOG WAS JUST BEGINNING to burn off when I parked beside Genevieve's car at the Ohlone Wilderness Regional Park. I surveyed the terrain, trying to ease my exercise anxiety. The park consisted of several large, grassy hills at the edge of the San Francisco Bay. The hills were surrounded by reclaimed salt beds that gave sanctuary to flocks of indigenous birds. It didn't look too intimidating. I spied Genevieve consulting a sign by the trailhead.

"Hi, Gen," I panted as I joined her. She turned from the map to hug me, but I held back, embarrassed by the sheen of sweat already on my brow. "Um, I haven't hiked in years," I ducked my head. "I'm already winded!"

"Don't worry," she said. "This is the start of my training for one of those big charity walk-a-thons. I just thought you might like an excuse to get some fresh air. I know how depression feels!"

I relaxed and said, "Thanks, it's hard to explain that to people." She smiled.

"How about this loop?" she pointed at the trail map. "In the middle, we can choose this other loop or come back to the lot." I did the math in my head. If we walked it all, it was five miles.

"Sounds good," I forced enthusiasm. We started out

slow, then picked up the pace as we approached the first big hill.

"How're the kids handling your being home all the time?" Genevieve asked. I had to meter my words to save my breath.

"Ed and I decided," I panted, "to keep them on their schedule, to minimize disruption. So, they're still going to after-care. That leaves my days free for whatever."

"You and the kids are so lucky to have someone like Ed supporting you," Genevieve said. The comment rankled. She adored Ed, who was a sort of life coach to her husband, Aaron. We'd known Aaron since he was a teen; his parents were our next-door neighbors for years. Ed encouraged Aaron to pursue a computer science degree when he was thinking of abandoning junior college. Aaron's parents breathed a sigh of relief when he followed Ed's advice to enroll at a UC school. The mantle of admiration they bestowed on Ed blocked me from revealing the truth to their daughter-in-law about "our" decision. The truth was, Ed insisted we change *nothing* about our lifestyle when I suggested the kids come after the final bell every day. He justified his position, wearing the same deer-in-the-headlights mask he'd worn at the appointment with Dr. Drexler. I recognized it was a poor financial decision, but I lacked the energy to argue.

"Yeah, I'm lucky," I agreed with Genevieve. We were climbing. Though the hill wasn't steep, the exertion took its toll. I headed off more questions that would force me to walk and talk at the same time, saying, "Tell me more about the charity race." Genevieve answered while I counted my inhales and exhales to slow the stitch developing in my side.

BACK IN THE SALON, Trina studied me as she adjusted her tie-dye boho skirt.

"You need a hydrating kelp-protein mask to hold the color in your hair and keep it moist," she diagnosed. "Can I start that for you?"

"How much is it?" I asked, acutely aware that I was already overspending.

"It'll be a hundred on top of your color and cut," she replied. I doubted that Ed would inquire, or even care if I told him, how much I'd spent.

"Yes, let's do it."

"Wonderful," she cried. I left her to masking and went back to thinking about Gen's and my conversation.

"SO, BESIDES WALKING," she said, "I started classes at that gym by the mall. Have you seen it?"

"The one with the bright yellow walls and all the mirrors and windows?" I clarified.

"Yes, that's it," Gen confirmed. "They have fun classes, like Zumba and the workout with the bouncing sticks," I shook my head to indicate ignorance. "You know, Zumba? It's a workout choreographed to salsa music and moves, like the old Jazzercise classes," she landed a couple of cha-chas in her hiking cadence. I recoiled, remembering Nana and her exercise obsession.

Gen added, "The sticks are for core work and arm strength." It all sounded like torture, except the dancing part. I used to love to dress up and dance for hours in the tiled foyer of our house with the yellow kitchen.

We arrived at the crossroads, and Gen said, "Wow, we're already here! Wanna keep going?" I did not. I wanted to run home. I wanted to lose myself in a medley of too much ibuprofen and Klonopin. I wanted to chase the high that was denied to me by the psych drugs that were supposed to be making me feel better! But I couldn't. I felt Gen's drive to push on.

"Sure, let's go," I smiled, fearful she'd think less of me if I chickened out now. The soles of my feet burned. Twin blisters burgeoned on my heels. "How hard are these dance classes?" I asked, sucking wind. "Maybe I ought to try one," I wished my mouth would shut up!

"Oh, my god! Yes, you'll love it," she threw her arms wide with delight. "I'm in the beginner Zumba class Friday at two. Meet me there!"

THE DRYER BUZZED AGAIN, announcing the end of my hair's five-star meal.

"One more rinse, then we'll cut and dry!" Trina trilled. While she sprayed warm water on my hungover head, I recalled Ed's and my conversation over breakfast when I arrived home from Ohlone.

I SHOVED HALF a slice of thick, buttery cinnamon toast in my mouth and chewed. I'd already told Ed about my walk with Gen, bringing him up to speed on our Zumba plans. He smiled at my animated excitement. Gen was right, I thought. I was lucky to have him.

"I don't think Dr. Basu likes me," I said after swallowing.

"What makes you think so?" Ed asked. I felt his wariness. Or was it weariness? Either way, I could tell he didn't want to hear my theory. Regardless, I told him about the appointment. Unlike prior occasions when I aired my suspicions about doctor biases, this time, Ed was on my side.

"That's *not* the right way for her to treat you," he said. "She's supposed to be adjusting your medications. We can't wait. This is torture!" He was almost more emotional over Dr. Basu's poor bedside manner than I'd been.

"I'm gonna do what she says," I told him. "I'm going to exercise. And, I want to color my hair."

"What color?" he was overtly wary now.

"Dark red, kinda auburn, I'm thinking?" I said. "Maybe a few highlights. Something natural but different."

"Oh, okay," he sounded relieved. He'd never forgiven me for coming home with a short bob one month ahead of our wedding. Before, chestnut waves cascaded over my shoulders, and Ed always joked it was his second-favorite feature of mine.

"It's *my* hair," I said, petulant. "I don't have to ask your permission for any of this, you know!"

"I know you don't, but thank you for telling me anyway," Ed smiled. "I love you."

I melted and said, "I love you, too." We chewed our cinnamon toast in silence.

"Do you think the new hair color will help you feel better?" Ed asked.

"Yeah, I could do with a makeover," I nodded. "I want to see something I like in the mirror."

"Shell, don't say stuff like that," he moaned.

"Like what?"

"I like everything I see when I look at you," he protested.

"You always say that! I'm talking about liking *myself* in the mirror," I wanted to explain that I was doing this for me, but it seemed selfish. Lydia's face loomed in my mind. I ignored her and stood up to grab Ed's unsuspecting face in my hands. I kissed him deeply.

"Whoa," he breathed. "Do you wanna—"

"Yes," I dragged him down the hall to our bedroom. This time, it was Lydia's tongue I imagined when he went down on me. I came hard with him between my thighs.

"FLIP YOUR HEAD, LIKE THIS," Trina turned off her handheld dryer to demonstrate, interrupting the remembered afterglow between my husband and me. I mimicked her, flinging forward to point my crown at the ground. Piles of unfamiliar hair stirred around the base of the chair. Trina scrubbed her fingers vigorously on my hot scalp. "Okay, now flip up fast," she instructed. I obeyed and caught the first look at the new me in the mirror.

Tousled auburn curls spilled, framing my face into a Botticelli painting. I'd forgotten I was so naturally curly. For years, I dried my hair iron-straight, adopting a severe look for the business world, on my father's advice.

"God, you're gorgeous," Trina admired, tweaking copper spirals. Surprised at the depth of feeling in her, I peered at my reflection more closely. I'd lost a few pounds, and it was apparent in my chins. My green eyes were wide open. Perhaps they were a little vacant, but I looked good, especially with my lumpy body obscured under the black salon cape.

"Wow," I breathed in compliment of her artistry.

"Right?" Trina agreed. "Look at this hair! Could I ask for a better canvas to practice on?" she demanded of the salon at-large. Everyone cooed.

TWENTY MINUTES and $500 later, I raced out, slammed the driver's door, and revved my engine. Somehow, I arrived at the gym with five minutes to spare. I circled to find Genevieve's car. It wasn't there. I parked and made my way inside, battling the urge to turn back when I saw a dozen dancers warming up at the barre. A corpulent woman chatted with several more students at the front desk. I hung back.

"Hi, I'm Luciana, the owner," she called me forward. "Welcome to Utopia Fitness!" Luciana collected my fees and gave me the rundown. By the time she finished, the teacher was calling us to order. Gen still hadn't arrived. I found a space at the far back corner of the studio, near enough the door that I could slip out without bringing attention to myself.

"Welcome, I'm Jilly! I see new faces," hollered the teacher, a teensy slip of a woman. "Find a space in front if this is your first time," I didn't move. "Come on, don't hide in the back," she pointed at me. I forced my feet to obey when they itched to flee. The music thumped. I claimed an empty space behind Jilly, who tapped her toes forward and backward. My self-consciousness evaporated. There was no time to think about anything except where I was stepping and what I was supposed to do with my arms. It helped that everyone else seemed to be struggling, too. Sweat poured down my neck. I slowed my feet every few repetitions to catch my breath. Genevieve slipped into the line behind me.

"Hey, I didn't recognize you," she stage-whispered, beginning to cha-cha. "Your hair is gorgeous! I'm sorry I missed you before class. My Reiki training went over." There was that word again! I lost track of what I was supposed to be doing. Jilly danced over to me.

"Like this," she demonstrated. I had to focus to keep from falling over my own feet.

Miraculously, I made it through my first Zumba class. After, as we mopped sweat and gulped water, Genevieve explained her tardiness.

"I'm getting certified in Reiki," she said. "My final level one class was today. Everyone hung around after to practice on each other." Jilly walked up.

"Great job today," she high-fived Gen, then turned to me. "You were amazing," she said. I wished she wouldn't hold up her hand for me to slap. I hated high-fives; I always mistimed them. Jilly's eyes raised, and her arm started to follow, but something stopped her. I remembered the tattoo moment with Lydia.

"I had a lot of fun," I said sincerely. "I'll be back, for sure." Jilly smiled and went to rally the troops for her next class. Genevieve and I collected our things.

"What's Reiki?" I finally asked. "My doctor mentioned it. She wants me to learn it." We started walking.

"You totally should! Reiki is amazing," said Genevieve. "It's energy healing using the hands. I found out about it from Kris's oncologist. I decided to learn so I can practice on Kris while she's having radiation and chemo." Kris was Gen's mother-in-law and our former next-door neighbor. Aaron was her son. Gen was caring for Kris following her cancer diagnosis.

"Weird that doctors recommend it," I was inclined to dismiss the whole subject. Hands-on healing reminded me of holy-rollers or some kind of cult. We waved goodbye to Luciana as we passed the front desk, crowded with students lined up to pay.

"Want a healing session?" Genevieve offered. "Reiki helps with depression and anxiety. I wouldn't charge you or anything, just so I could practice."

"Yeah, maybe," I allowed.

"Want to try another class with me?" Gen waved a purple legal-size schedule between us. "I was thinking about the POUND! Workout on Saturday. You remember, the one I told you about, with the sticks?"

"Definitely! See you then," I surprised myself with real enthusiasm. We hugged and went our separate ways.

CHAPTER 8

*A*fter leaving the Utopia Fitness lot, I headed to pick up the kids from school. Paused at a light, I realized I wasn't mired in what-ifs. It felt good to have pretty new hair and a plan to get better. I recalled the same feeling of well-being after the hike with Genevieve. My mind skipped back to the afterglow moment in bed with Ed, following our breakfast of cinnamon toast.

"THAT WAS UNEXPECTED," he chuckled when we were done. "I guess Dr. Basu was right about exercise, after all," he waggled his brows up and down suggestively like Groucho Marx.

All business, I said, "Dr. Drexler wants you to come in for an appointment. We talked about you the other day. She told me a story about her husband and son." I explained the rest to Ed. Part of me expected him to balk.

He was tight with his parents, and they were dubious about our treating Eddie's ADHD. I could only imagine the ration of shit to be endured from his dad, a retired naval officer, if Ed told them he was undergoing the same treatment. "What are your thoughts?" I asked when I was done. Before he could reply, I started justifying. "You might be happier if you were treated! I've read up on adult ADD. You have all the symptoms—"

"Shell, stop," he was lying on his side, watching me talk.

"Okay," I slumped sideways into the mattress, anticipating an argument.

"Don't look so defeated," he smiled. "I happen to agree with you. It's a great idea, and I'm thankful you took it to Dr. D on my behalf. Honestly, I've been thinking the same since Eddie's assessment. There are too many similarities between his behavior and mine for it not to be true!"

"Oh, thank goodness," I clasped my hands under my chin. "I thought you might be mad."

"Not at all. Will you make the appointment?" I was so relieved he hadn't argued that I didn't even mind his asking.

"Sure," I smiled. "Another thing I need to do is see Dr. Holliday. I need to his clearance for vigorous exercise."

"Do you need clearance for more 'vigorous exercise' with me?" he exaggerated the insinuation.

"Ed, cut it out!" I wanted to power through the list that was stuck in my head. If I waited too long to speak it aloud, I'd have to write it out a dozen times to erase its traces from my memory banks.

"Yes, ma'am," he saluted. I hit him with my knock-it-off glare. "Sorry. Please continue," he said.

"Dr. D wants me to take a class, like meditation or yoga."

"Another great idea," Ed enthused. "Good thing the kids are still enrolled in after-school care," he joked. "You're gonna be busier on leave than you were at work!" His words triggered a cascade of memories. My mind skipped from the impossible demands of my job, to missed vacations, to moments curled like a fetus on the restroom floor, to the humiliation of the videoconference room.

"What's that supposed to mean?" I snarled.

"What d'you mean, what's that supposed to mean?" his eyes were wide.

"The point of leave isn't for me to be busy! It isn't like I said, 'Gee, I want debilitating mental illness so I can learn to meditate.' This isn't fun; there's something really wrong with me."

"I didn't say you were doing this for fun," Ed explained. "But, I am happy you get to do the things you've missed, like running. And I'm super excited you have time to figure out your next career steps."

"Never mind," I sighed, feeling the pressure of his expectations.

"Don't say never mind, Shell," he kept me on the hook. "My point is, you don't have to go back to Jay's Little Shop of Horrors if you don't want to. You can do something different." I was about to chew him out for ignoring Dr. Drexler's injunction against career talk, but he shocked me into silence when he added, "Maybe this is our chance to do what we always talked about; to have one parent stay home with the kids. That way, you can go back to school for whatever you want!" The pressure was unbearable.

"We can't do that," I exploded. "I can't go into another line of work because we can't afford for me to go to school! Medical school is the only thing I want to do, anyway. That takes too long and costs too much. I can't believe I let my dad coerce me into getting a business degree," I smoldered over thwarted dreams. Then, I delivered the bitter afterthought, "Who would take care of the kids when I'm in class, even if we could afford it? You won't watch them as it is now," I opened my empath sense to Ed's reaction. I felt nothing, so I went for the jugular, "None of this would be an issue if we'd moved to Wisconsin when Patrick offered me my dream job!" My only prize was the injured look on Ed's face. Remorse flooded me, but I withheld apology.

Ed chose the high road, saying, "I'm gonna ignore that because we've been over it before. Your problem is, you see the challenges as roadblocks. They aren't," he reasoned. "We can figure this out together."

"What 'we,' Ed? You never follow through," I'd had it with his rosy outlook. "I get that the agreed-upon division of labor when we got married was that I'd manage our finances, but I can't anymore! The mess is too big. You actually have to *do* something to help me!"

"I have an idea," he said. "Let's make an appointment with Barry! He always finds a way to help." Barry was our financial advisor, who also advised most of my relatives. He'd helped Ed and me do a reset of our finances a few years ago, enlisting my mom and Matt to float us a consolidation loan after a family business we were in with my dad went south. My mom alluded to this loan over the summer when she complained about our buying two BMWs.

"I don't know," I hedged. It was tempting to lay our troubles on Barry, whom I expected would carry them to my mom, again. I suspected my mom wasn't going to keep playing ATM forever. However, I felt better having a plan, whether or not it panned out. "Prepare to get yelled at; Barry's not going to like the mess we've gotten ourselves back into."

Heartened, Ed said, "Nope, he won't like it, but this time we're gonna fix it for good!" I wanted to believe him.

"You promise you're on board? You're going to call Barry with me and help with the bills every month?"

"Yes, I promise," he answered solemnly. I felt niggling doubt.

"That means you have to stop using our credit cards for work, and you have to fill out your expense reports on time," I turned the screws, trying to assuage my worry with extracted promises.

"Yes, I know, Shell," he was getting annoyed.

"Don't take that tone with me!" I said. "You're just as responsible for this mess as I am."

"I promise," he held up his right hand as if to swear an oath in court. He looked uncomfortable, lying on his side facing me. "We got into this together, and we're going to get out together."

"Okay," I was mollified. "I'll make the appointment with Barry."

Remembering Ed's and my pact reinforced the good feelings from my new hair and Zumba. I parked at the kids' school and walked to the after-care portable, reveling in the slinky curls that bounced around the edges of my face. Elsie spied me from the playground and came running to fling herself into my arms.

"Momma, you're so pretty," she crooned, fingering my new locks.

"Thank you, sugar," I squeezed her and scanned the crowd of kids over her shoulder, looking for Eddie. Close behind Elsie followed Ms. Suzie, head of the on-site program.

"Hi, Suzie," I greeted.

"Hi, Michelle. I like your hair," she smiled. "May I have a word with you?"

"Sure," I answered, dread awakening. "Elsie, please go get your things and wait by the stairs."

"Eddie had some trouble today after homework hour," Suzie reported as Elsie skipped away. "He hit one of his friends. Another friend hit Eddie, trying to defend the first friend."

"What was the disagreement over?" I knew it would involve the Pokémon cards we allowed Eddie to bring to school today.

"Pokémon cards," she confirmed.

"I'm sorry, Ms. Suzie," I sighed, all the good feelings draining away. "I appreciate your patience while we work on his medications with his psychiatrist."

"I had to fill out an incident report," she informed me. This would mark Eddie's third incident report of the school year, and we were barely in the second month! "And, I need to remind you, six incident reports in one semester results in expulsion from the after-care program," Suzie recited the rules.

"Thank you for the reminder," I blushed. I was about to apologize again on Eddie's behalf, but something she said bothered me. I asked, "Are the other boys also getting written up?" Suzie's back stiffened.

"No, because Eddie was the aggressor," she said. I waited in silence, precisely as I'd learned from my first mentor in the investment banking world. Suzie fidgeted. "The parents of the other boys are being told about the incident," she offered. "We plan to keep the three of them separated a few days. Also, no more Pokémon cards at after-care, until further notice."

"I see," the first rule of negotiation, my mentor taught me, was to allow your opponent enough rope to hang themselves. I felt Ms. Suzie's apprehension swell.

"I guess I can see why you might expect the boy who hit Eddie to be written up," her voice trailed off.

"Exactly," I nodded sharply. "If my son was on the receiving end of physical aggression, he deserves to be protected. I'm relieved to hear you're writing up the boy who hit Eddie. I would hate to have to go to the program director."

Flustered, Ms. Suzie's mouth opened and shut a few

times like a fish out of water, then she said, "Of course, we want Eddie to feel protected. There's no need to involve the program director."

"Thank you for your help," I said sweetly and headed to the portable. My victory over Ms. Suzie was pyrrhic at best. A year ago, I would have crowed the story with great relish at one of our weekend parties. Today, I realized I had to reckon with my son's escalating behavior, or he'd end up expelled, not only from after-care but from school altogether. I arranged my face in my 'angry Mom' mask and mounted the stairs. Eddie sat at the time-out table. Elsie kept him company. She looked far more worried than her brother about what I might say.

"Let's go," I barked. The kids jumped, trotting to keep up with my furious speed-walking. By the time we were buckled in the car, I was in a towering rage. "What's wrong with you?" I unloaded on Eddie, glaring at him in the rearview mirror. "Why'd you fight over Pokémon cards? Especially after I convinced Daddy to let you bring them! I'm so upset right now, I don't know what to do." Eddie began to cry.

"I'm sorry, Mom," he sobbed.

"Why'd you do it, Eddie? Why?!"

"I don't know!" he wailed.

"You must have a reason," I insisted. "Answer me. What happened? Tell me exactly!"

He began to explain, "Ammar and me were playing Pokémon. Frankie was watching us. Frankie kept telling us what cards to play, and it was making Ammar mad—"

I interrupted with, "I fail to see what this has to do with you! Who did you hit?"

"I hit Frankie because he kept telling us what cards to play," Eddie tried to answer succinctly.

"How many times have I told you, Edward?" I shouted. "Just ignore people who're being jerks! Why do you care what Frankie says? He can't play your cards for you!" He said nothing. "I don't want to hear another word until I tell your father about this," I reached for the worst punishment possible for my hyperactive, imaginative fourth grader. "I want you to go to your room, sit in the middle of the floor, and don't touch anything! No toys, no books, no talking, until Daddy and I come talk to you."

"Okay, Mom," he said in a small voice.

"Do I have to go in time out, too?" Elsie asked.

"Mind your own business," I warned her.

WHEN WE GOT HOME, the kids hung their backpacks on the hall tree and scampered away. I went to find Ed. I could tell he was listening to a conference call, but he was also working on the screen array. I flagged him.

"Wow! Your hair! I love it," he gave me two thumbs-up. When I didn't react to the compliment, he slid back one headphone. "What's up?" he asked.

"Eddie got in trouble at after-care today," I said. "Over the Pokémon cards, of course."

"Darn it, Eddie," Ed lamented. "Did you find out from Ms. Suzie what happened?"

"Yes, I have to tell you about that—"

"Just a sec," he held up a finger. "They asked me something." I backed out and went to stare into the fridge. I thought I heard Elsie chattering. Wondering if she'd snuck into Eddie's room to keep him company during time out, I went to investigate. I crept noiselessly, sliding my feet along shiny hardwood boards. Elsie started talking again. She was in her own room. I stopped to press against the outside of her door frame.

"What's wrong with you?" For a second, I thought I was caught, but she went on, "I said, what's wrong with you, Black Bear? Why did you steal Brown Bear's cookie?" I detected the muffled sounds of stuffed animals being manipulated. "Answer me, now!" she commanded. I crouched in a question mark, shrinking from the reenactment of my anger. "That doesn't make any sense," my daughter whisper-shouted at her play family. "How many times have I told you, Black Bear? You don't steal cookies!" I could hear her smacking something. Curiosity got the best of me. I slid around the door frame to watch Elsie act out the scene. She was holding the hapless Black Bear upside down and beating his rear end with the open palm of her hand. She turned him upright to set him across the tea party table from her. "I'm so upset, I don't know what to do," she sighed dramatically. Fully absorbed in play, she didn't see me even when she looked up. My stomach flip-flopped. Hearing my words played back to me through her childish devices was terrible, but seeing her 'angry Mom' mask when she looked up, so exactly what I knew mine looked like, appalled me. I fled.

Behind our bathroom door, my trembling hands cradled the Ziplock. Months had passed since I tasted its forbidden fruit. I reached for an OxyContin bottle. I had to block that scene of Elsie on her bedroom floor! But, what if I died from mixing medications? What if the Oxy screwed with my antidepressants and made everything worse? What if—

Someone knocked.

"Shell, are you in there? Why's the door locked?" Ed spoke through the crack.

"I'm looking for something under the sink," I sounded far calmer than I felt. "Out in a sec!" My hands shook as I fed the pills from my palm back into the bottle. I replaced the Ziplock in its plain-sight hiding place and opened the door. "What's up?" I played innocent.

"Do you want to finish talking about Eddie?" Ed asked, confused by my light tone.

"Oh, right," I nodded. Heart still pounding, I motioned to the bed. "You might want to lie down for this." Ed laughed appreciatively, but I recognized our shared exasperation behind his laughter. I shut the bedroom door and relayed everything, from playground to front doorstep. I hid my face in the pillows and moaned, "I was so mean to him! I didn't even let him finish explaining."

"You can't blame yourself," Ed said. "Eddie's psychiatrist told us it's normal for boys his age with ADHD to struggle with self-control. We let Eddie take the cards to school. He proved he can't handle it. What should his punishment be?"

"He was already in time out most of the afternoon," I pleaded.

"He's gotta learn, Shell. Maybe grounding him from Pokémon cards for a week will do the trick," Ed pushed himself off the bed. "Let's talk to him. Oh, before I forget, I have to go on a quick trip. Leaving Sunday, back Tuesday." My heart skipped.

"I thought you talked to your manager and got all your travel canceled through year-end?"

"This is a quick trip," he placated. "There's no one else to do it, or I wouldn't have agreed."

"Ed! You promised," I reminded him. We faced off on opposite sides of our king bed.

"Shell, there's nothing I can do about it. I've gotta keep my job, don't I?" he appealed. "I'm doing everything I can so you don't have to worry about money coming in."

"What's that supposed to mean, *I* don't have to worry about money coming in? *You're* supposed to be helping with the finances, too!"

"I didn't mean it like that," Ed huffed.

"Fine, let's go talk to Eddie," I went to the door. Ed rushed to prevent me from escaping, using his stiff arm over my head as a stopper before I could open it wide.

"Shell, please," he said. "I don't want to spend the weekend with you all huffy and butt-hurt."

"Oh, I'm huffy and butt-hurt?" I said, pulling the doorknob to no avail. "I'll show you huffy and butt-hurt! Let me out. We're going to deal with our son, and then I'll make your dinner like a good little wife," I ignored that the kids could overhear all of this through our cracked door. "Let me out, now!" I gave the door some slack, then yanked it hard against his outstretched arm.

"Ouch," he said, giving me a dose of satisfaction. "Calm down, please."

"Let me out, and I will!" I rejoined.

"Shell, I don't want to fight." I released the door handle and twisted to face him. The door clunked shut. He kept it pinned under his palm.

"It's all about what you want, isn't it?" I sneered. "Does it matter what I want? I don't feel right, Ed. I can't think straight. You going on a business trip makes everything bigger and scarier!"

"I'm sorry you're feeling so bad. I don't want you to feel this way. What can I do?" he asked. When I opened my mouth to suggest he stay home, he rushed to say, "Besides staying home from this trip!"

"Forget it," I said, dejected. "I'm used to bending over backward for your career."

"Shell, don't say that. That's not how I want you to feel!"

"It doesn't matter how you want me to feel," I said harshly. "It's how I feel," voicing my true feelings like this was equally terrifying and empowering. Part of me wanted to throw my arms around Ed and apologize. The other part wanted to turn the screws again.

"Mom?" Eddie's muffled voice called. "Are you and Dad coming? I've been sitting here the whole time like you told me to. I promise I didn't touch anything!" I looked expectantly at Ed, who was still standing over me at the threshold of our bedroom. He nodded his assent and removed his arm.

"Yes, sweetheart," I called and pulled the door open. Ed and I walked into Eddie's room together, presenting a united front that was little more than lipstick on a pig.

CHAPTER 9

*M*y alarm chimed early the morning after the Pokémon incident.

"What?" Ed's muffled voice floated over the great wall of pillows. "What time is it?"

"Time to get up," I groaned. "We have to eat before Eddie's first game," I kicked off the covers. Today marked the official start of flag football season, and we were staring down the barrel of an 8 a.m. doubleheader. "Shit," I exclaimed.

"What now?" Ed hadn't budged.

"I totally spaced on telling you! Gen asked me to meet her at Utopia for a class this morning. Would you mind taking the kids to football without me?"

"Absolutely, you should go," Ed stretched. "What time's your class?"

"Nine to ten," I said. "But I might want to stay for yoga. It goes to eleven."

"'Turn it up to eleven!'" Ed quipped. "You know?" he prompted when I didn't say anything, "up to eleven?

Like *Spinal Tap*?" I sighed heavily, wishing he'd stick to the subject. He got the message. "After the games," he stood up, "we can meet you at the phở place, to celebrate the start of Eddie's football season," he headed for the bathroom.

I felt a shade of guilt. I didn't love football the way Ed and his family did. They lived and died by the BCS. Already, Grandpa Black was foretelling Eddie's college career. Seeing Eddie on the gridiron, surrounded by boys who were a full year older than him because he was a year young for his grade, triggered my basest motherly instincts. Games morphed into nail-biting, cuticle-ripping torture sessions. Every play, I expected him to hit his head and never wake up again. The feeling of worry overtook me now, in our bedroom, nary a pigskin in sight. I shouted at Ed's retreating back, "I can't miss Eddie's game!" I jumped out of bed, wild-eyed. "What if he gets hurt? What if he needs me?" Ed turned and looked at me with consternation.

"Shell, what are you worried about? One, it's flag football, *and* they wear helmets and pads. No one's getting seriously injured. Two," he enumerated, "Eddie isn't going to care whether you're there or not. All he cares about is playing with his friends. I'll be there if he needs anything. And, three, you've done your duty at practices. Go to your class."

I chewed on the inside of my cheek, then said, "But I feel bad! Like I'm skipping out on something I should never want to miss."

"Don't be ridiculous," Ed absolved me with a wave of his hand. "You've been to all of Eddie's games of every sport. Now, it's time to follow doctors orders. You're motivated. Gen expects you. Get going." I still hesitated, so he added another push. "I got this. Really. You seem to forget that I've been getting the kids ready for school every day since day one! I know how to take care of them," he smiled teasingly.

"Okay," I tried to relinquish my panic. It settled but didn't fade. "I can do this," I affirmed, more for myself than for Ed.

"I know you can, and before you know it, you'll be all better and back at work," Ed cheered me on. I ignored the twinge of irritation his words teased up.

"I'll meet you at the phở place about noon," I said in a stronger voice.

"Eddie will love that," Ed turned to shower. "See if you can get seated with his favorite server," he called over his shoulder.

I turned the other way and called over my shoulder, "I'm going to get the kids up." I started walking but made a U-turn after Ed closed the bathroom door. I grabbed the Xanax bottle from my nightstand, the one that held my insomnia-battling doses. I took two.

"I'm sorry, Michelle," Luciana called across the studio. "We're not going to hold the yoga class since not enough students showed." I pushed myself up and knelt to roll my mat. There'd been a half-dozen students in the first class, including me and Gen. I was the only one still present.

"I'm so bummed," I replied to Luciana, who was

ambling around the desk. I didn't want to go to half a football game. Behind her, I saw the teacher shove open the door and head toward the parking lot. "Does this happen often?"

"Oh, you know, it depends on the week, the class, the teacher, the weather," she laughed a short, unamused laugh. She stopped beside me. Her energy felt like a funeral.

"Business is hard to predict," I surmised with a friendly shrug. "I was in a family business that, by all rights, should've been a massive success. Only the timing was wrong," we walked together as I put away my mat, and she made her rounds, flipping off the lights. "There were a lot of students in class yesterday," I encouraged.

"Yeah, but football season starts today, from pee-wees up to high school," she worried. "Business drops off on Saturdays, so I have to shift to Sundays if I want to keep my clientele. Moms don't mind missing NFL games, but they never miss their kids' games." She sighed, "I hate the transition! My instructors complain every fall."

"Oh, that's rough," I realized belatedly, I was a mom with a bye. "Hey, Luciana, let me get out of your hair," I gestured at the door. "My husband took the kids to football today, so I could come to class."

"Thanks for showing up, Michelle," she waved and locked the door behind me.

I didn't drive to the city park where Eddie's second game was underway. I drove home instead, debating the whole time. I didn't want to be one of the unmotherly-mothers alluded to by Luciana. But I also didn't want to let another day slip by without following up on the clue I remembered at the hair salon. I pulled in the driveway and checked the clock. Forty-five minutes to spare.

THERE WERE a lot of Lydia Gormans, I quickly discovered. I added 'Los Gatos' to my search; I remembered her son was a public school student there. Zero hits. Refusing to entertain the possibility of failure, I changed the location to California, then combed through the results one-by-one. None of the pages I clicked through were helpful.

I switched to Facebook. Again, my search revealed a large number of Lydia Gormans in California. I scrolled. Most of the profiles featured unfamiliar faces. A few loosely matched my remembrance of Lydia. Some didn't have a picture. I checked every last one, hoping to unearth any small clue.

All of a sudden, I jumped out of my chair and punched the air.

My patient scrolling yielded results in the form of a Lydia Gorman Spandau, who lived in San Jose, and whose profile picture featured the seal of the Air Force Reserve. The stories Lydia shared from her years in the AFR came rushing back. I'd listened to her tell them raptly, reveling in the tales of clandestine lesbian experimentation in the barracks. I chuckled and licked my lips as I perused her Facebook page in reverse chronological order.

There was Bill; I remembered him from a picture she showed me before. He looked much the same. Lydia was heavier than I remembered. An unfamiliar boy who appeared to be about Eddie's age, or rather younger, stood by her, Bill, and a lanky youth in a recent family picture. Like Benjamin Button, I watched the boy age in reverse as I scrolled. Lydia's occupation was listed as a store manager for a regional coffee chain. The last I recalled, she'd been in project management for a high-tech firm in Silicon Valley. A million questions sprung to mind.

Lost in my voyeurism, I didn't watch the time. Ed called.

"Hello?" I answered, distracted.

"Hey, the game's done," the garbled sounds of kids cavorting and adults shouting bled between his words. "You already at the restaurant?"

"Oops, not yet," I glanced at the time. It was five after noon!

"Well, don't worry about it," he said. "The Baxters want us to come over this afternoon. The kids and I'll meet you at home. Oh, and I agreed to bring some stuff," he rattled off our meal contribution.

"We'll have to stop at the store on our way," I said. "I'll make a list." We bid each other goodbye. Staring into Lydia's still-open Facebook profile, I considered what methods were at my disposal to summon her. The screensaver engaged in a fractal pattern. I watched its tiny tendrils grow and spin off the side of the screen. I decided I wasn't going to drink today. I needed insomnia tonight.

. . .

THE FRONT DOOR slammed as I climbed out of the shower. I swathed myself in a bathrobe and went to greet everyone.

"...and then, Coach put Eddie in as quarterback!" I heard Ed enthuse into his phone.

"How many passes did he complete?" I heard my father-in-law ask eagerly.

"How many touchdowns did he score?" I heard Ed's mom at the same time.

"Just a sec," Ed tapped the mute button and passed me Eddie's muddy football uniform. "I'm on the phone with my parents," he stated the obvious. "They couldn't wait to hear the highlights. Eddie had two great games! He paid attention and followed the coach's instructions." I breathed a sigh of relief. I'd held my fingers crossed that there was no repetition of Eddie's troubles from after-care yesterday. "I'm going in the office to finish talking," Ed said. I pursed my lips at him in warning. "What?" he asked.

"We have stuff to get done if you want to go to the Baxters," I said. "You can't talk to your parents all day!"

"I know, Shell, I'm just gonna finish telling them about Eddie's big plays," he protested.

"Fine, I guess I'll do everything," I stomped down the hall but halted when I remembered the dirty uniform in my hands.

"Anyway, as I was saying," Ed's voice faded as he walked to the other end of the house. I changed my trajectory.

Poking my head in Eddie's door, I asked, "How were your games?"

"Hi, Mom. They were great! I played quarterback for a whole half," he gave me the rundown. Hearing it retold by my intact son was far less anxiety-provoking than being there in person. Eddie concluded with, "And now my day is perfect because I get to go to Ryder's house!" He pointed to an overstuffed duffel bag at his feet and asked, "Is it okay if I take all of my Nerf guns?" We negotiated a reasonable haul of weapons, and I went to check on Elsie. In the hallway between their doors, I paused. I could still hear Ed in the office, laughing with his parents. I looked at Elsie's almost-shut door. I could hear her debating with herself behind it.

"Eavesdroppers never hear any good of themselves," when I heard Nana's voice, I almost fell over! She might as well be standing next to me; that's how clear and real the words were spoken. I revolved in a circle to make sure I was alone. I stopped to listen when Elsie started talking again.

"Lila can play with *this* doll, and I can play with *this* babydoll," she said. "But, oh, dear. What if Lila doesn't want a brown-haired doll? Her hair is blonde! What if she won't play with me because she doesn't like my toys?" I shivered. The air conditioning was blasting down the neck of my robe. I tightened it and proceeded to the laundry room. As I passed the office on my return trip, Ed emerged and nearly smacked into me. The phone was clapped to his ear now.

"Yeah, she's right here," he said. "Do you wanna

talk to her?" I waved him off wildly. I didn't want to talk to my own parents, let alone his! I lived in dread of the very uncomfortable conversation I was going to be forced to repeat with all three sets of parents before long. "No, she wasn't at the games today, remember? I told you, she went to an exercise class." A moment of silence on his end. "Yes, like Jazzercise," he responded and listened again. "Well, it was ordered by her therapist! It isn't like she wanted to miss the games," he defended me. I flailed my arms to indicate my wish for him to shut up. "Here, hold on, she wants to talk to you," he misread my gestures. I shook my head hard in the negative. He nodded just as hard back at me, holding the phone out. I snatched it from his outstretched palm and touched mute.

"Don't do this to me," I said belligerently. "I'm not ready to talk to any of the parents yet!"

"Shell, they just want to say hi," he encouraged. "You don't have to tell them about your leave today, but you're gonna have to tell them sooner or later. In any case, they know we're getting ready to go to the Baxters. This'll be quick."

"Ed, now is not the time," I pleaded.

"You might as well start talking," he put his hands behind his back.

"Hello?" I heard Ed Senior ask into their end of the phone. "Michelle, are you there?" I gave Ed the nastiest look I could and unmuted.

"Hey," my phony greeting was too loud. I sounded like my dad talking to the next-door neighbor dad that day after he dropped me from the diving board. "How're you two doing?"

"We're so excited about this quarterback grandson of ours," answered Grandpa Black. "Proud as pie! But, why are you skipping football for exercise class? That doesn't sound like my daughter-in-law," he poked fun.

"Ed," interjected my mother-in-law. "It's proud as a peacock, not proud as pie," she delivered the correction with gentle good humor.

"How about proud as purple?" he guffawed. "Might as well get used to it! Our Eddie's gonna be the greatest quarterback the Huskies ever had." I rolled my eyes hard, even though Ed was standing by me, vicariously enjoying the conversation. I hated the pressure on my son! Ed Senior had a tendency to overstate everything, I reminded myself. He meant no harm. It was my customary practice to smile and agree. Today, however, I lacked my customary patience.

"Eddie doesn't have to—" I started, but Prudence beat me to the punch.

"Eddie doesn't have to do anything he doesn't want to, including play football," she informed her husband. "Quit pressuring!"

"Jeez, Prue," Ed Senior's hair-trigger temper switched on. "You mothers! It isn't like Eddie's on the phone. I'm not telling him what he can or cannot do. I just see that he's a talented player, and he loves the game. I'm excited for him; I'm not signing him up for classes at U-dub!" I couldn't listen to them bicker.

I cleared my throat and said, "Yeah, I was bummed I couldn't be at the games. It sounds like he had fun. Hey, listen, we need to get going—" was as far as I got before Ed Senior remembered his question.

"Ed told us these exercise classes were ordered by your doctor. What kind of doctor orders Jazzercise?" he teased.

"Ed," admonished Prudence.

"I'm done with physical therapy and ready to graduate to full activity," I lied to hurry things up. "These Zumba classes are low intensity enough for me to start with."

"I read an article about Zumba the other day during my morning news hour, you know when I sit in my office with my coffee and go through email?" Prudence explained needlessly. Every time she referred to her morning news hour, she was careful to tell her audience — whether someone new to her or someone she'd known for decades — what she meant. This tendency necessitated lengthy periods of waiting before she got to the point. I chalked it up to her self-effacing personality, her habit as a Navy officer's wife, or her ardent wish to make everyone around her comfortable at all times. It was tough to distinguish between these competing motives; she was adept at hiding her true feelings.

"Oh?" I prompted, afraid I'd missed a conversational cue.

"Well, the article said that Zumba is the best cardio you can get. It combines the benefits of running without the wear and tear on the joints," she shared.

"Zamboo? Zembob?" guessed Ed Senior. "What're you calling it?"

"Zoom-buh," I enunciated carefully.

"Huh," he was stumped. "Is it like martial arts?" Prudence and I laughed.

"It's part salsa-dancing, part calisthenics," I put it in terms that would make sense to him.

"Oh! That's all you had to say. See how smart my daughter-in-law is?" he boasted. "That makes perfect sense."

Ed, who'd apparently been able to hear both sides of the conversation, leaned his head over to yell into the microphone, "You only say that because she's the only one who speaks 'Dad!'" We all laughed.

"I need a Dad translator. How much do you charge, Michelle?" I was surprised to hear Prudence join the roast. It felt good to laugh with them.

"Okay, we gotta go," Ed continued to project his voice into the phone I held. "The Baxters are expecting us."

"Have fun, talk to you later, love you," everyone called out at once.

It was midnight when I parked in our driveway.

I looked at the kids in the rearview mirror and said, "If you want to go back to the Baxters tomorrow, go inside and get ready for bed while I help Daddy." Over dinner, Ed and Dan had devised a scheme for us to watch the Broncos-Raiders game the next day at their house. Kickoff was 5:30. Ed's flight for his work trip left at 9 p.m. I said it was too much to jam in. Dan suggested Ed pack early and bring his suitcase with him so he could depart from their house. Ed said we could do that if we drove two cars over. Having overheard our discussion, all four kids entreated me on their knees to consent to the plan. I didn't want to be the killjoy! I capitulated, then had to sneak to the bathroom to swallow enough Xanax to quell the panic that ascended from my stomach into my throat. "I'll come tuck you in shortly," I said before I got out and went around to the other side of the car. The kids scampered past, Eddie lugging his duffel of Nerf guns and Elsie cradling the two blonde dolls she and Lila played 'house' with.

"Shell, just let me sleep here," Ed moaned when I unlatched his seatbelt and started maneuvering him so he could stand up and lean on my shoulders. I pressed my lips together and said nothing. I managed to hoist Ed out and lead him up the path to the front door. Once in the foyer, I got behind him, aimed him down the right hall, and gave a gentle push. I watched him carom off the mahogany-paneled walls a couple times before I went to retrieve our kitchenwares from the car.

"Good night, Elsie," I tucked her in after dropping the dirty dishes in the kitchen.

"Good night, Momma," she murmured. "I love you. You're so pretty!" she petted my hair, reminding me that I had an agenda to attend to. I hugged her tight before I moved to the next room.

"Good night, Eddie," I smoothed his hair.

"Night, Mom," he yawned. "I can't wait to go back to Ryder's tomorrow! Thanks for taking us." I smiled and kissed his forehead. My brain prickled with irritation at the reminder of Ed's thoughtlessness. Still, my empath sense purred, feeling my son's appreciation and excitement. The conflicting emotions made me a little unsteady on my feet, or perhaps it was the drugs.

In our room, I discovered Ed, still fully-clothed, face-planted across the bed.

"Get up," I stood between his legs, which stuck over the side of the mattress like a pirate ship's plank. I shook him. "You have to shower! I can't sleep with you smelling like this," I complained.

He gurgled, "Please, Shell, let me sleep."

"Ed, get up," I picked up one leg in each arm and started dragging him toward me.

"Nooo," he groaned. I dropped his legs, and his toes touched the floor. His torso slid overboard. He ended up on his knees, neck bent, head sideways against the mattress, like a giant rag doll.

"Ed, please," I begged. "You know how much trouble I have sleeping!"

He drooled a little as he lifted his head to say, "Okay, can you please start the shower?" I went to crank it up. When I returned, he was starting to look a little green around the gills.

"It's warming up. Come on, get up," I steadied him under his armpits. "You need to undress."

"Okay," we managed to get his feet under him.

"I'm going to finish putting things away. I'll be back in a few minutes," I headed out the door, passed the kitchen, and turned on the lights in the office. I logged into Facebook and picked up reading backward through Lydia's posts where I left off. There were a couple of photos from about three years ago that captured my attention, in particular.

One was captioned, "Me-n-Tasha, 2 peas in a pod!" In it, Lydia smiled, shoulder-to-shoulder with a woman who had a short, curly razor cut. They both wore ugly Christmas sweaters. I felt a spark of envy. I clicked the second, posted six weeks before the Christmas one.

"The new gal pal in my life!" the caption blared. "We just met on Halloween, and already we're inseparable," followed by a mishmash of love and friendship emojis. I read all the posts in between, and then all the way back to Halloween, before the gal-pal post. There were no other mentions of this woman, who was not tagged in either photo. I scrolled back up to the after-Christmas posts, which I'd read in the morning. Rereading, I saw them in a different light.

Right after the first of the new year, Lydia had written a rambling post about the passing of the seasons, how the tinsel on the tree got crinkly and tangled, then fell off the boughs. The first time I read it in the morning, I thought she had too much wine and was waxing poetic. Now, I saw it for what it was: they must have broken up! A few more morose posts followed through January and February. Finally, in March, there was a happy post. Lydia was with the two boys. The young one was dressed as a leprechaun.

"Shell," Ed yelled from the other end of the house. "Shell, come here!" he sounded scared. I closed the browser and ran to see what was the matter. I tripped on his discarded clothes but caught myself and skidded around the corner into the tiny bathroom. I almost smacked into Ed's naked backside. He was pointing up at the mildew spots around the top of the shower.

"Spider!" he gasped, pointing harder.

"Ed, there's no spider," I said. "That's mold."

"Look," he insisted. "Spider!" I squinted down the length of his finger. Sure enough, a spindly, dime-sized spider lurked among the green-black velvet dots.

"Oh, my god," I bellyached. "Give me a break. Just kill the stupid thing!" I yanked a few squares of toilet paper off the roll and shoved them at him. I'd accepted his arachnophobia along with our wedding vows. Back then, I thought it was cute. But being the only spider slayer in the family grew irksome over the years, and I hated that the kids had absorbed his fear.

"Will you do it for me?" he asked, not taking his eyes off the eight-legged invader.

"Fine," I shut off the water and clambered onto the gray plastic shower bench. I smashed the spider, climbed down, and restarted the water. "Are you happy?" I showed him the pulverized remains.

"Thank you," he wobbled a little on his feet. "You're my hero!"

"It's not like it was Shelob," I said. "Finish your shower. I'll be back in a few minutes."

"I should help you clean up," he started to follow me.

"Ed, take your shower! You've gotta get up and pack in the morning so we can go back to the Baxters, remember?"

"Oh, that's right," he slurred. "I'm sorry." I sighed. Often when Ed got blitzed and started to feel the comedown before passing out, he'd apologize endlessly. I hoped we weren't headed for one of these bouts.

"Why're you sorry? Just go take your shower."

"I'm sorry!" he repeated. "I really enjoy hanging out with Dan. I missed him while we were estranged."

"Yeah?" I folded my arms. "I noticed you didn't have any trouble volunteering me to drive an extra car over and manage the kids after you leave."

"I'm sorry!" he looked stricken. "I didn't think about that. I'm sorry," he hiccuped softly.

"Stop saying you're sorry," I said crossly.

"I'm sorry, Shell," he clapped his hands over his mouth when I gave a murderous glare.

"Just. Take. A. Shower!" I pointed at the steam billowing from the bathroom door. Accentuating his motions, Ed about-faced military-style, hands still ostentatiously affixed to his face. He goose-stepped, à la the Ministry of Silly Walks, into the cloud. I had to laugh when he peeked out around the frame of the door from inside the bathroom. He dropped his hands, smiled, and withdrew his head. I waited until I heard the sound of the water change from the hard plinking of drops on plastic and tile to the softer pattering on human flesh.

I dashed back to the office, got into Facebook, and sent a friend request to Lydia.

CHAPTER 10

*L*ate Sunday morning, I checked Facebook. Nothing yet. I sat there, what-iffing and picking my cuticles. The kids were playing in the backyard while Ed packed at the other end of the house. I heard him coming and switched windows before he walked up behind me.

"What cycle on the new washer for underwear?" he asked.

"Same as always," I said, exasperated at having to repeat two-year-old instructions.

"Shell," he sighed. "I'm sorry, I can't remember! I need to make sure there's enough time for everything to dry."

"Okay, let's go," I led the way into the laundry room and pointed to the dizzying array of buttons. The back patio screen went *swish-ka-chunk* while I showed Ed how to program the load. The kids appeared. Our ancient, buff-and-white, ugly-faced dog dangled from Eddie's arms.

"Mom," Eddie interrupted. His psychiatrist advised us to ignore these interruptions, then explain after the fact why we ignored him.

"—but you have to push this button—" I continued.

"Mom!" Eddie spoke louder. "We have to tell you something."

"—to make sure it's the shortest cycle possible," I finished my sentence and turned to my son. "Edward, I was speaking. Do not interrupt!"

"Momma," Elsie looked anxious. She rarely interrupted. Even as young as she was, she already navigated the intricacies of human communication better than most adults. "We didn't mean to interrupt, but Minnie is sick!" I looked at the well-loved bag of bones in Eddie's arms.

"Put her down," I said. When he did, she slumped to the floor, reminiscent of Ed the night before. I looked at Ed.

"Shit," we said in unison. Minnie's breathing was labored, and she was in some kind of doggie-trance. I squatted and ran my hands over her. She flopped her tail once before it fell to the floor.

"What should we do?" I looked up at Ed. I couldn't think. He squatted beside me and put a hand on Minnie, too.

"Take her to the emergency vet?" he guessed. Eddie and Elsie started to cry.

"Is Minnie going to be okay?" asked Eddie.

"I don't know, sweetheart," I didn't want to give false hope.

"I don't want Minnie to die," bawled Elsie. "I miss

Aslan!" I choked up. When I'd graduated from college and moved to my first apartment in Denver, I couldn't wait to get a dog of my own. Ed, still finishing up his extended senior year in Seattle, generously offered to buy me a puppy, as he said, 'to hold his spot till he moved in.' When I went to inspect the first litter, one pup pranced out of the laundry basket while the rest held back. He looked like a tiny stuffed toy, with his splotchy mop of white-and-sable fur and squashed face. He clambered into my lap. When I picked him up and tucked him against my neck, he nibbled my lobe then stuck his microscopic tongue in my ear. I called Ed on my way home, crying that I was in love, but I couldn't get a dog. My apartment complex didn't allow pets. Ed, intent on giving me what I wanted, insisted I go for it anyway. Aslan died three years ago.

"Don't worry, sugar," I comforted Elsie. "You and Eddie come pet Minnie while I get dressed." They obeyed. I crooked a finger for Ed to follow me. Behind our bedroom door, I said, "I can't handle a replay of what happened with Aslan."

"Well, since we don't have travel plans coming up, you don't need to worry about that," Ed said cautiously. He knew I was apt to lose emotional control when we were on the subject of Aslan.

"It was my fault we went to Sonoma! We should've stayed home and taken him to the vet," I moaned. I was still lashing myself for not being with my beloved pet when he died. All I could think about was how alone and scared he must have felt without me.

"Shell?" Ed got close to check my face.

"I'm okay," I sniffled. "I don't think we should drag this out with Minnie."

"What do you mean?"

"She's old. We don't even really know how old because we got her at that shelter. She's got all those weird growths. And, she's had fainting spells before," I didn't want to say the words.

"You're saying you want to put her down sooner rather than later?" Ed said them for me.

"Yes," I whispered and covered my eyes. He was quiet for a moment.

"I think that's the right thing to do," he agreed. "Who's going to take her to the vet?"

"You're packing. I'll do it," I said, straightening my spine. "We're taking two cars to the Baxters, anyway. I'll meet you there after." I went to carry my burden to the car.

IN THE LAUNDRY ROOM, I discovered the kids had ginned up a soft pallet for Minnie, made of blankets borrowed from the living room couch. They were preparing to siphon droplets of water into her slack mouth with a straw.

"Why're you doing that?" I asked, curious.

"Minnie's thirsty. She was panting," Elsie explained, prying Minnie's upper lip back so Eddie could feed the straw between her sparse teeth.

"C'mon, Minnie! You can do it," Eddie cheered desperately for his pet. It hurt my heart to watch them minister to her.

"Guys, I need to pick Minnie up and take her to the vet," I said.

"We want to come with," Elsie informed me.

"I'm sorry, you can't," I said, trying not to cry.

"Mom, it's okay," Eddie got up and hugged me. "I think she's going to be okay, look!" he pointed. Minnie struggled to lift her head. She gave up, exhausted with the effort.

"Guys," I took a deep breath. "Minnie's probably not going to be okay. She's pretty old like Nana was." I felt Eddie panic in my empath sense, and he backed away from me a couple steps.

"Mom, no!" he cried out. "No, no, no!" He and Nana had been thick as thieves, as the very young and the very old often are. She'd passed eighteen months ago, but he still talked about her at least weekly, recalling plastic lightsaber fights in the garden with her before Elsie was born. He fell against me and wailed. Elsie's chin trembled, and I motioned for her to join us. With my kids leaning on me, I tried to explain.

"Sometimes, when a pet is really sick, and there's nothing more the vet can do for them, we have to let them go."

"Why?" Eddie demanded. "I don't want Minnie to go!"

"Because it's cruel to keep them alive when they're in so much pain," I made the explanation simple for my two little nurses. They didn't object. "I wish I could've done the same for Aslan," I started to cry, too. Ed found us. Eddie reached out to pull him into the family hug.

"What's going on? I thought you already left," he said to me.

"The kids and I were just having a talk about," my voice trailed off into tears.

"Ah, I see," Ed said and hugged us tighter. Minnie stirred on the floor at our feet. I broke away.

"I better get her to the vet," I said, wiping away tears. "Everyone give her hugs and kisses." I gathered her up in my arms, including the blanket pallet, and drove off.

A COUPLE HOURS LATER, I strolled up the Baxters' front walk. Ed and Dan were drinking beers on the tiny front patio, enveloped in the mouthwatering aroma of smoking meat. When I came through the gate, they stopped laughing.

"Everything go okay?" Ed asked, searching my face.

"She lives to see another day," I was thankful I hadn't had to go through with it. "She's got a couple medications, and the emergency vet wants us to take her to our regular vet in a couple days," I elaborated.

"Isn't she, like, almost twenty?" asked Dan. I nodded. "It's so rare for dogs to live that long. She looked a little ragged the last time we were over."

"She's on her last legs for sure," Ed agreed. "I feel sorry for the kids! Now we'll have to go through this with them again when she really does go." I felt my culpability.

"What did you want me to do," I snapped. "Put her down when she was doing better?"

"Of course not, Shell!" Ed looked hurt. "I know you made the only decision you could. I'm just thinking about what a hard lesson it is."

"Oh, man, I remember when my first dog, Skipper, died," Dan told us. "He knew how much we kids liked it when he'd jump up from playing dead and tear after us around the yard," he laughed. "He'd let us tease him forever. One day, my mom found my brother and me poking him with a yardstick. He was stone cold dead, but we thought he was playing!" We all howled with laughter. "I'll never forget the look on her face when she realized what'd happened," he said, making a horrified mug. Cathy opened the screen door onto the patio and waved at me in surprise. She was hard of hearing.

"What're you all laughing at?" she asked and looked at Dan to read his lips.

"I told them about when Skipper died," he enunciated clearly.

"Why'd you tell them that when they just had to put their dog down?"

"They didn't," he repeated my news to her.

"Oh, sheesh," she shook her head. "The poor kids. What a tough situation!" I felt myself flush but didn't comment. "Shell, you want to bring your things in and sit down?" she led me to the kitchen, where I balanced my purse and coat on a barstool. We leaned over the island on our elbows to chat. I breathed deeply; I'd decided to come clean with her on my way over.

"Cathy," I said. "I owe you a long past-due apology. I apologized to Dan after our rift over the team. But, I never apologized to you," I was talking about the kids' team we'd co-founded so our boys could play baseball together every season. Ed and I rudely uninvited Dan and Cathy from being co-coach and team mom after allowing ourselves to be swayed by newcomers who eventually wrested the team from our control, too. "Ed and I treated you every bit as poorly as we treated Dan, and I'm sorry." She listened without comment. "I'm so thankful we've brought our families back together for the kids' sake because they don't deserve to be separated over our differences. I hope you and I can be better friends again, too." The trifecta of Xanax, Klonopin, and ibuprofen racing through my system was the only reason I could say this without losing my shit.

"Wow, Shell," she said, processing my words. "Ed apologized to me over the summer. I wondered when you would," the way Cathy said it, it lacked the chastising tone it could have had.

"I haven't been thinking clearly. That's my only defense," I shrugged.

"You *have* seemed stressed when we've seen you lately," she said, turning to start the potato salad. I was conscious of my abominable behavior at the Independence Day party when she put me in my place by turning down my invitation so pointedly. "Has work been a pain in the butt?"

"You don't know the half of it," I snorted, giddy that she seemed to have accepted my apology. I told her everything, starting with the indignity of the videoconference, but leaving out all mention of prescriptions and lesbian fantasies. It was good practice for the three-ring circus coming to town; I couldn't withhold much longer from laying all of this bare to the parents. By the time I wrapped up my story, the game was underway, and everyone was eating. Cathy put down her diet soda.

"Holy cow, Shell. I had no idea this was all going on. Why didn't you tell me? Or Jade? Or anyone?" she looked at me in wonder. "How'd you hold it all in?"

"Isn't that what everyone does?" I shrugged. "Besides, Ed knows. He's been there through it all."

"That's a lot for him," she looked over at the guys, yelling boisterously at the TV. "I remember what a hard time Dan had around my cancer diagnosis." I remembered, too. I'd hung out for hours with Cathy in the hospital while Dan worked and did single-dad duty. Ed and I helped ferry their kids around during her long months of treatment, as well. "How's Ed handling things?" she asked.

"Ed doesn't seem too bothered by this, except insofar as it's affected my ability to take care of my responsibilities around the house," I said tartly. "Sometimes, he acts like there's nothing wrong, and this is a vacation for me!"

"I'm sure that's not what he thinks," Cathy stood up and started collecting dirty dishes. I went to use the bathroom and sneak a look at Facebook. I almost shrieked when I saw the notification that Lydia had accepted my friend request! I clamped my hands over my mouth, and my elbow collided with a three-wick jar candle. It fell to the floor, where it shattered. I had to put my phone away and deal with the splashed wax and broken glass. By the time Cathy and I set everything to rights, it was time for Ed to leave for the airport. The kids could barely tear themselves away from playing with Lila and Ryder to say good-bye. I followed Ed out to his car.

"Oh, I almost forgot, I told my parents you'd let them know how Eddie's practice goes on Tuesday since I don't get back till late," he told me as we walked side-by-side.

"Why'd you volunteer me for that, too?" I whined.

"What do you mean, too?"

"Never mind," I sighed. "I'm not going to call them," my voice was stern.

"Shell, you've got to tell our families about being on leave! You can't hide it forever," he insisted.

"Why not?" I stuck out my lower lip.

"Because," he said. "I never know what I'm allowed to say to who!" Ostensibly, we were talking about my leave of absence. But I knew what he really meant. He detested the way I'd been telling partial-truths to my parents and forcing him to do the same with his parents on my behalf for years. "Please, Shell. You need their support, and I need them to know."

"I'll call them while you're gone," I promised. We hugged good-bye, and he got in his car. No sooner than the taillights' glow disappeared down the street, I rushed back inside to collect the kids. I found Cathy and Dan in the kitchen and told them, "I think we're gonna head out. I'm nervous about getting the kids ready for school without Ed home." It was a partial truth.

"Cathy was just telling me about what you've been

going through," Dan gave me a rough hug. "I'm sorry things have been so hard!" I teared up and nodded my thanks. Cathy stepped in to hug me next.

"Michelle, thank you for your apology," she said. "I've missed our friendship. I'm glad we talked! Call me anytime. You were there for me when I battled cancer. I'm here for you now." My tears spilled over, and I hugged Cathy hard.

"You have no idea how much that means to me, thank you!"

AT HOME, I shooed the kids into their Sunday night showers and sat at my desk. When I'd checked from the Baxters' house, there'd only been an acceptance notification. Now there was a message from Lydia, too! I teetered on indecision for the briefest second before opening it.

"Michelle," it read, "how lovely to hear from you! I can't tell you how surprised I was when I received your friend request. I looked over your profile. Wow, you've been as busy as me! A lot's happened since we met and lost touch. I'd love to catch up with you over a cup of coffee." My jaw fell slack. She'd made it too easy! I clicked reply and chewed a knuckle.

"Lydia," I typed, "thank you for accepting my friend request! I wasn't sure if you would after last time. I'd love to chat over coffee. You've been on my mind lately. When and where?" I hit send.

CHAPTER 11

*A*fter I dropped the kids at school Monday morning, I sat staring out the breakfast nook window at the driveway where I'd last seen Lydia. Half the night, I'd lain awake, trying to think up an excuse to avoid talking to the parents. The other half, I dozed between compulsive Facebook checks and bouts of worry over the hand under the bed, which surely sensed Ed's absence. Minnie padded up and stretched into a downward dog at my feet. She listed to one side.

"Do you have to go potty?" I asked, reaching out my foot to steady her. She trotted toward the living room, making it only a few feet before she tripped and keeled over. I rushed to her, but she scrambled up before I got there. "Don't die on me yet," I shook my finger at her. She smiled and begged to be let out in the backyard. I obliged, and she tore after a fat blue jay pecking our overgrown grass.

I went to the office to sit at my desk. I checked Facebook. Nothing.

I reached for the phone but stopped. Instead, I searched for Reiki training nearby. As Dr. Drexler mentioned, the parks & recreation department offered a class. I signed up for a session that began the next month, then rechecked Facebook.

I finally picked up the phone. Instead of dialing Ed Senior and Prudence, whom I'd selected to check off my list first, I called my orthopedic surgeon.

"Dr. Holliday's office," answered a familiar voice.

"I'm a current patient. I'd like to make an appointment," I crossed my fingers that the receptionist wouldn't recognize my voice.

"Mrs. Black," she greeted me unannounced. "I've been trying to reach you." I didn't respond. "Have you received my messages?"

"No, I'm sorry, I haven't," I finally said.

"I was calling to tell you we billed your insurance for your last missed appointment. They refused payment. You have to pay the fee before we process any further claims."

"I understand," I said. "I'll do that when I come in. Can you please transfer me to the appointment desk?"

"The fee is $150," she said. "I can take your payment information whenever you're ready." Gritting my teeth, I rattled off one of the credit card numbers I had memorized. "Would you like your confirmation code?"

"No," I clamped down on a smart remark.

"Thank you, have a lovely day," she said sweetly before patching me through. No sooner than I hung up from scheduling, Ed called.

"How'd it go with the kids this morning?" he asked.

"Fine," I said. "Eddie was dragging, but Elsie's excited about spirit week."

"Did you do her hair in braids, like she wanted?"

"I tried," I whined. "I can't do it like you can! It was super stressful, and I know I let Elsie down because I made them all lopsided."

"I'm sure she loved it, Shell," he said. "Quit putting yourself down." I harrumphed. "I'm serious—" he started.

"Spare me the lecture, Ed!" I interrupted. "Is there a reason you called besides checking on Elsie's braids?"

He was quiet a moment before asking, "Have you called any of our parents yet?"

"No!" I snapped. "I've been on the phone all morning with Dr. Holliday's office trying to get an appointment for my release."

"What do you mean, trying?"

"They wouldn't let me make an appointment," I explained what transpired with the receptionist. "I knew I wasn't going to get away with it, after the way she stalked me."

"'I want my two dollars!'" Ed quoted another movie. "'Give me my two dollars!'"

"Ed, I'm not laughing."

"'Why does the paperboy keep showing up and demanding two dollars from Lane?'" he continued the *Better Off Dead* charade.

"Stop it!" I yelled. "The missed appointment fee was a hundred and fifty bucks!"

"Okay, Shell, I get it," he finally stopped laughing. "When're you seeing him?"

"Next week. I also signed up for a Reiki course," I reported. "It's on Saturday mornings through the end of the year."

"Saturday mornings are perfect," Ed exclaimed. "The kids and I will have a blast together at football every week," he paused. "Are you going to call the parents now?"

"I haven't called Barry's office yet," I started making excuses. "And I have to call the vet, too!"

"Shell, those won't even take five minutes," Ed lost his patience. "That leaves over three hours for you to talk to the parents before you have to get the kids!"

"I need a break, Ed," I was desperate for him to acquit me, as he had with Eddie's game. "I can do the calls tomorrow," I bargained.

"Shell, you've *got* to tell our families about being on leave," he insisted. "I don't want to lie to them anymore." A Facebook notification popped up on my computer screen.

"New message from Lydia Gorman Spandau," it read.

"You're right," I slammed the brakes on my tantrum.

"Okay?" Ed drew the second syllable out in near-disbelief.

"Don't worry, I'll make the appointments, too! Good luck with your meetings, talk to you later," I rushed to hang up.

"Do you really mean it?" Ed caught me.

"Yes, Ed, I mean it. I want to get it over with. Can I go now?"

"Okay, text if you need anything," he said.

"Okay, love you, bye!" I threw my phone to the floor in my excitement over Lydia's message. I didn't chase after it.

Instead, I clicked and read, "Of course, I want to be friends. I always wondered what happened to you! Since you still live in Fremont, do you want to meet at the coffee shop by the hospital?" My guts rumbled with excitement. "I can get over there any evening this week, so you choose." I reread her message ten times, trying to imagine how I would do this without raising Ed's suspicions. I decided it didn't matter. I'd say whatever I had to say to get out of the house. I hit reply and started typing.

"I'd love to meet there. How's Thursday at 8 p.m.?" I hit send and waited a few minutes. Lydia didn't check it. My cell phone rang. I retrieved it from where it had fallen. The call was from our regular vet.

"Hello?" I answered.

"Hi, Michelle," greeted Amy, a tech who did dog-sitting gigs on the side.

"Hey, Amy," I said. "I was about to call you. We need to bring Minnie in."

"We got the ER notification," she said. "Tell me what's going on." I brought her up to speed.

I finished, close to tears, saying, "I think it's time to put her down."

"I'm sorry, Michelle," Amy comforted me. "For what it's worth, I think that's the right call. She's starting to get like Aslan was at the end." Amy had been sitting the dogs when we were on that fateful camping trip in Sonoma. She panicked when she arrived at our house one day to find Aslan unresponsive on the floor. I still felt the emotional echo of her experience; she'd tried everything to revive him, even administering CPR.

"Yeah," I whispered. "I know."

"Let's make an appointment for a few days from now," she said gently. "That way, you and the kids have time to say good-bye before you bring her in." I let her guide me through the planning process. "Okay, we'll see you Friday," she confirmed.

After we hung up, I rechecked Facebook. Lydia had read my message but hadn't responded. I sighed, then called Barry's office. I added everything to my calendar and forwarded invites to Ed. I created a new alternate email account for the sole purpose of communicating with Lydia. I paid a couple of utility bills, sending double the amount due so I could ignore them for at least a month. I sat at the kitchen table, staring out the window after picking at my lunch. Finally, I could no longer put off the dreaded phone calls. I dialed Ed's parents.

"Hello, Michelle?" answered Ed Senior.

"Hi, Dad," I said. "There's something I need to talk to you and Mom about."

"Are you okay? Is Eddie okay?" he reverted to calling my husband by his childhood nickname. It was so confusing with all of these Edwards!

"Yeah, Ed's fine. He's on a business trip," I assured him.

"Prue!" he yelled over the mouthpiece. "Michelle

needs to talk to us. Pick up!" I could hear him scrape the mouthpiece over his chin. "Are the kids okay?" he asked.

"Yes, everyone's okay," I reassured.

"Hello?" my mother-in-law picked up an extension.

"Hi, Mom," I greeted. Suddenly, talking was a lot harder. I plunged into my story. This edition was similar to the one I'd told Cathy, only it began in June with my ER visit on the drive home from San Diego. They listened in silence the whole time. When I was done, Ed Senior spoke first.

"How could anything be wrong?" he was incredulous. "Saturday, you sounded fine!"

"Ed," Prudence chided him. "Just because nothing sounded off last time doesn't mean nothing's wrong today."

"We talked to her," he persisted. "She even went to Jazzercise class!"

"Michelle," Prudence ignored him. "I'm so sorry to hear you're feeling this way. Have the medications started helping yet?"

"I don't know," I said. "It's hard to tell from day-to-day. If I look back a couple weeks, nothing seems too different."

"How long do the doctors think it'll take before you start feeling better?" she asked.

"I don't know," I said. "Dr. Drexler wants me to take off a minimum of two months."

"Two months!" ejected Ed Senior. "How could this take two whole months to recover from? You march back in there and tell Jay off," he encouraged me. "You could run the whole damn company. You're more than smart enough to!" I had nothing to say to this. Prudence was more tactful than her husband.

"It sounds to me like you're better off away from work for a while," she said. "What did you tell the kids?"

"That Mommy is taking some time off because she needs rest. They kind of get it; they've seen me struggling lately," I said.

"They're such smart, caring kids," Prudence said.

"What d'you think about the move the Fed made on interest rates yesterday?" Ed Senior asked out of left field, causing my heart to race. I didn't want to think about anything remotely work-related! But I didn't want to *not* answer him, either. I lacked the courage to tell him off the way I'd seen Ed do over the years.

"Ummm," my hesitation couldn't be heard over Prudence's exclamation, anyway.

"Christopher Edward Black," I'd never heard her use his full name to his face, not in twenty years. "Stop badgering Michelle. She just told us she's not supposed to talk about work!"

"Jeez, Prue," began the familiar refrain. "It isn't like she's on her deathbed, and I'm asking her to decide a Supreme Court case. It's a simple question!"

"Nevertheless, it's a question you're barred from asking. Leave her alone. I'm putting my foot down," I was even more surprised at her spirited defense of me than I'd been when she roasted her husband! Beating stage IV metastatic cancer had hardened and

137

emboldened her in ways I hadn't appreciated until now.

I cleared my throat and said, "I should probably get going."

"I hate to ask this," Prudence said carefully. "But you know how much planning in advance it takes when we live so far from the closest commissary — we have to drive two towns over —" I fought to stay focused until she delivered her payload. "So, what I'm asking is, do you think you'll still come to our house for Thanksgiving?" Agoraphobia gripped me. I didn't want to spend a week on an island with Ed's entire family, shoehorned into his parents' three-bedroom house! But I knew Ed was counting on our traditional week of vacation on Puget Sound. Prudence must have sensed my reluctance because she kindly backpedaled, "Never mind! There's plenty of time to discuss this. We can wait till your Ed's back from his trip."

"Okay, thanks," I breathed relief.

"We'll let you go," she said. "We love you. Tell the kids we love them, too."

"I still don't understand," Ed Senior said. "Michelle, you sound fine to me!"

"Ed, stop. We'll talk about this after we say good-bye," Prudence's word was final.

"Bye, I love you, too," I said. "Thanks for listening."

"Call us anytime," my mother-in-law said. "I promise, I'll keep Dad in line." Through the phone, I could feel the deep offense Ed Senior took at her words. I rushed our good-byes to avoid getting roped into their hostilities.

After hanging up, I stared out the front window some more. It was a grey day, and the rain that had begun falling looked like grey glue dripping from the sky. I went to let Minnie in. As I toweled raindrops off her fur, I weighed taking some Xanax before my next call. I decided to hold off. I finally dialed.

My mom answered, "Hi, honey, is everything okay?"

"Yes, Mom, everything—" autopilot engaged. I stopped. "No, as a matter of fact, everything is not okay."

"Is someone hurt? Are the kids okay?"

"They're fine. It's me," I said. "I've been diagnosed with depression and anxiety, and I'm taking some time off work."

"Oh, my God!" she squawked. "My poor baby! When did this happen?" I told her a slightly modified version of what I'd told my in-laws.

"Why didn't you tell me what you were going through?" she made no effort to soften the hurt in her voice. "You hid it from me for months!"

"Mom, I'm telling you as soon as I can," I'd been crying on-and-off throughout our conversation. The tears started to flow again. "Some days, I don't even know if I can get out of bed, let alone tackle a discussion like this."

"Shelley, don't you know, I'm your mother, and I want to help? If you'd told me what was going on, I could've helped!"

"Didn't you notice anything wrong with me in the summer?" I jabbed. "I told you how unhappy I was,

139

and all you did was complain about the money I owe you!"

"That's not true, Michelle," she said hotly.

"Yes, it is! You freaked out and told me I had to keep doing everything no matter what, and oh-by-the-way, what about the money I owe you?"

"I thought I was helping talk you through a difficult time," she said. "You're always so with it, and on top of things, how would I know you were in trouble? If you hadn't hidden the truth from me, I would've acted differently!"

I didn't have it in me to argue anymore, so I said, "Is there anything else, Mother?"

She thought a moment, then said, "I just don't know what you'll do for money. Pop and I can't afford to support your family!" Instead of hanging up and running for the Ziplock like I wanted, I buttoned down the sadness I'd hoped my mom would soothe and stepped into the ring with her.

"Did I ask you to support us?" there was acid on my tongue.

"No, but what will you do for money? You live too high a lifestyle for—"

"I tried to tell you over the summer, Mother," I used the most withering tone I could manage. "I will receive disability pay—"

"That was for knee surgery," she cut in. "This is *mental illness*!" she made it sound like I had leprosy. "What're you going to do if work finds out? What if you can't ever get a job again because you have this history?" I wanted so badly to throw the phone across the room, on purpose this time! It was agonizing for my scariest what-ifs to get dragged into the light after the weeks I'd spent squaring them away into the dark corners of my mind, learning to ignore their chatter between doses.

"This is a new disability claim," I explained through gritted teeth. I told my mom everything I'd learned from my HR department so her anxiety would be laid to rest. "They have to give me my job back when I'm ready to return in twelve weeks," I concluded.

"They're not going to hold your job that long. They need someone doing the work! That Jay wouldn't know a rating agency if it walked up and slapped him in the face. How're you going to *make him* let you come back?"

"Why are you so fixated on my going back there?" I lost my temper. "That job is what did this to me! Why do you want me to worry about it? What about how I feel!"

"You used to love that job," she lamented. "What if you don't like anyplace else as well? Or you can't find as well-paying a position?" As had happened so often lately when interacting with my mom, something in me snapped.

"Why can't you just tell me you love me? And you hope I feel better?" I thundered. "This isn't my fault! I didn't choose it, just like Juliet didn't choose her illness. But you always blamed her, too, didn't you?"

"How could you say that?" my mom demanded. "What happened to my sister wasn't her fault. It was that downright bastard Dominic Abner who did this to her! If he hadn't abused her during their marriage, she wouldn't —"

"Mom, you can't blame Dominic just because he's a man. It isn't automatically a man's fault when something goes wrong for a woman!"

"Michelle, you are too young to remember. I was there. I witnessed it. I'll never forgive him, just like I'll never forgive your father!" Another shrouded memory tore through the fabric of the moment, and I lost track of what she was saying.

"SHELLEY, PLEASE COME HERE," Dwayne called when I arrived home from freshman swim practice one afternoon. I shut the front door. It was odd for him to make a direct request of me; he usually only responded when I spoke to him. I followed the sound of his sonorous voice to find his 6'6" frame hovering over a glass of ice water on the drop leaf breakfast table. Sweat beads crusted the glass in a diamond pavé. A few had run down to form a perfectly puffy, clear life preserver around its base. Dwayne's giant oil-stained hands rested on either side of the glass, uncharacteristically still.

"Hello, Dwayne," I greeted awkwardly. My mom rarely invited her boyfriend to the house when she wasn't home. "Where's my mom?"

"She went to pick up Juliet. Your grandmother needed her help." I knew Nana had checked Juliet into a hospital a couple days earlier. My mom told me that

142

the police found Juliet wandering in her pajamas on a neighborhood street at dawn, babbling about secret societies and being watched in her bedroom. When they got hold of Nana as next of kin, they sent her to Juliet's home, where she found my two young cousins alone in the house, asleep in their beds. After Nana dropped them at school, my mom said, Nana did the only thing she could do; she had Juliet involuntarily committed. I didn't know what that meant, and I didn't inquire.

"When will my mom be back?" I asked Dwayne.

"Pretty soon," he checked the wall clock. "She said we should order pizza and wait for her."

"I was gonna hang out and eat at Lynn's," resistance crept into my tone. "She got the new Violent Femmes CD!" Dwayne's swarthy face looked uncomfortable.

"Shelley, I think you should wait here until your mom gets home," he said. An argument sprung to my lips, but I heard the front door open. Dwayne stood to urge me out of his way. I hustled to precede him into the TV room, where we found Juliet and my mom locked in a staring contest. Juliet jumped like a gunshot went off when Dwayne and I came around the corner. She wobbled to-and-fro, her brown irises floating in a sea of bloodshot red.

"What's wrong with you?" my mother was scolding her sister. "Mom shouldn't have to raise your kids, Juliet. She's done enough for you!" My mom's blue irises swam in frustrated tears.

"I don't know," Juliet whispered in a super-slow-motion reply to my mom's query.

"Just take your medicine," my mom wailed. "Don't

listen to the voices when they tell you not to!" I watched the waltz of the two sisters, hypnotized by the back-and-forth of my mom's bossy impatience and my aunt's disconnected defiance.

"Denise," Dwayne leaned down to drop a kiss on my mom's lips. "Shelley just got home. We didn't order the pizza yet." My mom's watery eyes turned to me.

"I'm so upset right now, I don't know what to do," she vented. "Can you just go order the pizza? I'm starving, and I have to take Juliet to a different hospital after we eat!"

"I want to go to Lynn's," I said.

"Not tonight, Shelley," she was adamant. "I can't keep track of you running around, too," she cast a sideways glance at her sister, who stood rooted to the same spot. "I have to go change. Order the pizza now," she started down the hall toward her bedroom. Dwayne followed her, leaving me alone with my Aunt Juliet.

"Do you want some water?" I asked, casting about for a suitable topic of conversation. She looked at me, a spark of recognition igniting, then fizzling, in her face.

"Who are you?" she whispered.

Stunned, I said, "I'm Shelley! Your niece?" Juliet still looked clueless. "I'm Denise's daughter. You know? Your kids are my cousins?" Still nothing.

"Yes, I want some water," Juliet said, her voice creaking like rusty door hinges.

"Okay, come with me," I held out my hand. She took it and trailed me to the kitchen. I handed her a full glass. She stared at me, still unsteady on her feet, and narrowed her eyes.

"Can you hear that?" she asked. The house was silent, save for Dwayne's deep bass tones rumbling behind the closed bedroom door.

"That's just Dwayne in my mom's bedroom," I said. Juliet set her glass of water down and leaned conspiratorially toward me.

"There are voices in the radio," she darted her eyes in the direction of the TV room.

"I don't hear anything, Aunt Juliet," I said, after listening a few seconds.

"Shh," she put a finger to her lips and turned to walk away. "They're listening to us." My hackles raised as I followed her.

"The radio only works one way," I said forcefully, trying to curb my fear with bravado.

"No," she whipped back around to look at me. "These voices are put there by the aliens." I wasn't sure I heard her right.

"Aliens?" I repeated.

"Yes, they travel by electricity. You can't plug anything into an outlet," she was suddenly manic. "We have to unplug everything! Why didn't you do that before? Now, they know we're here," she dropped to her knees and scrabbled at the cords behind our oak entertainment center. Dumbfounded, I watched her make her way around the room, unplugging every appliance. My mom and Dwayne joined us.

"Juliet," my mom snapped. "What are you doing?"

"We have to unplug everything," Juliet smacked one fist into the other palm. "They can follow us through electricity!" I couldn't help it. I laughed. My mom spun to face me.

"Shelley! Why is she doing that?" she demanded.

"I have no idea," I giggled. It was my unfortunate reaction to extreme stress.

"Denise, there are aliens in this equipment," Juliet pointed at our stereo, prompting gales of laughter from me.

"Quit laughing!" my mom shouted. Dwayne rested a hand on the nape of her neck.

"Denise," he said quietly, "Shelley doesn't understand what's wrong with Juliet." My mom looked at him, lips pressed together. She looked at me again, and I could see creases in her forehead. She went to her sister.

"Juliet, come sit on the couch," she intoned in her best high-school-teacher voice. "Shelley, go order the pizza." I was holding my breath, still trying to smother nervous laughter.

"I'll order the pizza," Dwayne volunteered. "Shelley, go to your room if you need a minute," he smiled at me with his gap-toothed grin. I escaped to splash cold water on my face. When I returned, Dwayne was alone in the TV room. I could hear my mom on the phone in the kitchen and see where Juliet floated like a ghost by the kitchen door.

"Have a seat," Dwayne indicated the couch opposite him. I did so reluctantly. "Your mom is a pretty simple person," he began. "She loves what she loves. She hates what she hates. She does it all with her heart on her sleeve." I tried to imagine my mom as he described, with her actual heart affixed to her sleeve, blood spurting from the severed aorta in a shower that spattered everyone nearby. "She's stressed because she has a lot going on," he explained what my mom had not. "She's teaching full-time. She's studying for her graduate exams. Juliet won't accept Nana's assistance, so it falls to your mom to care for her. You're smart, and you have a cool head. I hope you use it to make things easier for your mom rather than harder."

"I'm used to being my mom's mom, if that's what you're talking about," I tossed my hair.

"That's not what I meant—" he started to say.

"Who are you?" Juliet had ghosted her way to stand behind me. "I don't recognize you. Did you come with," she dropped her voice to the smallest of whispers, *"the aliens?"* Another giggle fit threatened. Dwayne stood up and went to put his hand on the nape of Juliet's neck like he had with my mom.

"Let's go, Juliet. Your sister's in the kitchen. It's safe there," he guided her away.

I REALIZED I could hear my mom sobbing through the phone. I was still sitting in the same spot at the kitchen table, grey glue dripping from the gutters and sky.

"I'm sorry I didn't know you were hurting, Shelley," she cried. "I love you, and I want you to feel better!" Fatigue dragged at me.

"I know that, Mom. I love you, too. I'm sorry I didn't tell you sooner."

147

"When do you go back to the doctor?" she sniffled.

"I go back to the psychiatrist tomorrow, and I have two therapy appointments this week."

"Will you call me after every appointment and tell me everything the doctor said?" she asked.

"I'll call you later this week," I evaded, hoping this wasn't a preview of her expectations for the duration of my leave. We said good-bye.

I went to take a nap. I didn't even need pills to help me fall asleep.

CHAPTER 12

That evening, Eddie poked his head in the office where I sat, typing.

"Mom," he said. "Mom!"

"Eddie, I told you, I'm in the middle of something."

"Mom, that was, like, an hour ago," he walked up beside me, and I switched windows. I glanced at the clock.

"Sorry, sweetheart, I was too focused," I stood up and hugged him. It was after seven on a school night. I hadn't even begun to think about dinner.

"It's okay, Mom," he smiled brightly. "Me and Elsie were playing, but we're hungry." Elsie peeked around the door.

"We're hungry!" she echoed. Dinner would be followed by clean-up, which would be followed by bedtime prep.

"How about McDonald's?" I offered. It was the quickest path back to my desk.

• • •

Twenty minutes later, in the drive-thru, my phone rang. I debated letting it go to voicemail.

"Hello?" I answered, juggling drinks and Happy Meals.

"Hi, Pal, it's your dad and Charlie," he greeted at the same time Charlie called out, "Hey!"

"Hi," I was half-distracted, half-impatient, and wholly sorry I'd answered. "The kids and I are picking up fast food for a treat since Ed's on a work trip."

Dad read my tone and said, "We don't wanna interrupt! We're just returning your call. Call back when you have time."

"We love you! Hey, kids, we love you," Charlie shouted. "Can they hear me?" she asked.

"I'll put you on the car speaker." The four of them chatted as I drove. The other line rang.

"Ed's calling to say good night to the kids," I told my dad and Charlie. Everyone rushed their good-byes. I switched over.

"Daddy!" the kids yelled before he could say hello. By the time they'd satisfied his questions about school and homework, we were parked in the driveway.

"Guys, take your food and go eat in the kitchen. I'll be there in a minute," I instructed.

After they slammed their doors, Ed said, "Late dinner, huh?"

"I was busy filling out my medical history online!" I snapped.

"I'm not criticizing, Shell," he said patiently. "It's just that they're usually in bed around this time. They'll survive one late night." I felt bad for my hasty reaction.

"How'd your day go?" I asked.

"It was a whirlwind," he said. "We just got back from wining and dining the client," while he described their extravagant, expense-account-paid meal, my mind wandered. I was dreading another night alone, at the mercy of the hand.

When he stopped, I said, "I miss you a lot. I'll be happy when you're back tomorrow."

"I miss you guys, too," he said. "But I've got bad news. I have to stay through the end of the week. My manager wants me on-site till we're sure everything's right." I didn't say anything. "Hello?" I remained silent. "I know you're probably upset with me—"

"You promised!" I yelled.

"I know I did, but I can't control this," he protested. I started to hyperventilate. "Shell, calm down," his voice surrounded me in the car, suffocating instead of making me feel safe. "You're going to be okay."

"How would you know?" I gasped. "You aren't here!"

"Have you taken your meds today?"

"Yes, of course," I was offended. "I'm not a child!"

"Have you taken an extra Xanax? Remember, Dr. D said you need to take it when you get like this?" I knew for sure I'd taken two of the big ones and four of the little ones in pursuit of sleep last night, but I couldn't remember how many I'd taken today after my nap. I was afraid I'd never wake up again if I took enough to blot out the terrors tonight.

"Ed, I want you to come home," I moaned. "Please!"

"I can't, Shell," he said. I wrestled with my panic until I could speak without crying, yelling, or begging.

"I don't want to do this alone," I finally said.

"You're not alone. I'm right here," he yawned. "I've got an early start tomorrow morning. Better head to bed."

I was quiet for a moment, then said, "Fine," with no discernible intonation.

"Did you get dinner for yourself?" he asked as an afterthought.

"Yes."

"You should go eat while it's hot," he encouraged. "I'll call you tomorrow when I have a break."

"Fine," I said.

"Alright, I love you, good night," Ed said.

"Fine, good night," I said in the automaton's monotone. Ed hung up.

IT WAS ALMOST ten o'clock when I tucked in the kids. I changed into pajamas and hovered in the bathroom, trying to drum up the courage to open the cabinet door. Infuriated with my cowardice, I grabbed the pills I was allowed to take and went to the kitchen to retrieve my chocolate shake from the freezer. I unwrapped my Double Quarter Pounder with Cheese. It was totally unappetizing in its congealed state. I popped a couple fries in my mouth, but they tasted like stone-cold styrofoam. I trashed the fries and washed down the pills with a scraped-up spoonful of semi-frozen shake. It was bland. I transferred it to the blender and added large pours of Irish cream, coffee liqueur, and vodka, then whirled till it was milkshake consistency again. I gagged at the first taste but got accustomed fast as the alcohol and drugs seeped into my bloodstream. I sipped the concoction at my desk while I reread the draft email I'd hidden when the kids came to find me before dinner.

"The bouncy house post is from my daughter's recent birthday party. She was born about a year after you and I lost touch. What a coincidence we both had our second kids around the same time! A boy for you, a girl for me. Ed is fine, thank you for asking. He's been at a different job for about three years now. We're past due for him to switch things up, LOL." Last time, Lydia had been keenly interested in Ed's career. She hoped their professional paths would cross, though they were employed by different Silicon Valley tech giants. Her hope struck me as silly; Ed was in sales, and she was in project management. No way they'd ever end up in the same place at the same time. I finished the email off by adding, "I'm looking forward to Thursday. I'll meet you at the coffee shop."

I hesitated over what closing to use. Was 'love, Michelle,' too committed? Maybe 'hugs, Michelle' was appropriate. I settled for the agnostic, 'see you soon, Michelle.' It felt stilted, but I hit send. I engaged the screen saver then sat back to watch the fractal patterns. Pretty soon, I shook the mouse to dispel them and started typing an email to our sitter. This one was quick, which was good because the spiked shake had awakened my hunger.

I shut off the office lights, nuked my burger, and pan-fried a pile of tater tots. As I munched on my refurbished meal, I watched my guilty-favorite movie, *Imagine Me & You*. In it, a bride walking down the aisle toward her groom on her proud father's arm glimpses an unfamiliar woman sneaking out at the far end of a pew. The stranger is the bride's florist, unbeknownst to her because of being hired by a well-meaning but overbearing mother. Their eyes lock for a fleeting second while time stands still. When the bride introduces herself to the florist in the reception tent after the ceremony, her picture-perfect life is turned upside-down. The two women are drawn to each other; obviously, they're soulmates. But what could the straight, newlywed woman do? Somehow, I felt the story was about me, but I never knew who to imagine in the florist role.

By the time the credits rolled, I was tired and wasted enough to brave the empty bedroom. When I gained the safety of the bed, I turned out the light and built the wall of pillows. I rested my distended belly on them. I would have to do four Zumba classes, I thought, to work that meal off. I giggled in the dark and passed out.

I FROZE, crouching in the grass beside my mom.

I heard the noise approaching from far, far away. It was almost like I felt it in my bones, well before its distinct chopping beat could be discerned by human ears. I dropped my miniature metal spade and went to stand under the patio cover. It was the same patio, beside the same pool, with the same diving board my dad dropped me from. This must have been an earlier time; the row of spiky Italian cypress trees that lined one side of our backyard was shorter than before.

"Shelley, where are you going?" my mom asked, pushing up to her knees. "Come back and help me," she pointed to where I'd abandoned our excavation. The thumping got loud enough for my dad, who was spreading mulch in the corner, to hear it.

"Denise, I'll take care of this," he announced. He grounded his shovel in the hard-baked desert dirt and walked toward the patio. I scooted backward, butting my behind against the door that led into the bathroom as Daddy got closer. My mom stood on her feet now, watching us with one hand on her hip, the other dangling a dandelion weeder.

"Come here, Shelley," my dad said, reaching out a gloved hand. I shook my head no. "What are you hiding from?"

"The hopter-copter," I lisped, pointing a chubby index finger up at the sky. It was getting louder.

"There's nothing to be afraid of. The helicopter can't hurt you," Daddy said. "Come out here and watch when it flies over." He was at the edge of the patio.

"No, Daddy," I reached a blind hand above my head, grasping backward for the doorknob.

"Do not open that door," he said. "Come here, now!" I pulled my hand down and covered my ears. The whop-whop-whop of the regional hospital chopper, whose landing approach took it directly over our house several times a week, petrified me.

"No!" I wailed. "No, hopter-copter!"

"It's a helicopter," my dad was in front of me now, gripping my tiny recalcitrant forearms. He tugged, trying to uncover my ears. "Say it correctly. Say, hel-i-cop-ter!"

"NO HOPTER-COPTER!" I yelled as loud as I could, battling to keep my hands over my ears. I squished my eyes shut. He dragged me, kicking and screaming, into the backyard just as the gigantic, terrifying insect flew close overhead. I scrambled to get away, begging, "Daddy, no! Please, Daddy!" He held me in place, his Daddy fingers digging into my arms, "Ow-ow-ow!" My mom rushed over.

"Jay, that's enough! You're hurting her," she sliced her hand like a knife between my dad's face and mine, severing some invisible cord. He flinched back as if she'd struck him, then jumped to his feet, dragging me halfway up with him.

"Don't you dare touch me!" he shouted in her face. "I'm teaching my daughter not to be a coward. Keep your nose out of it!" My mom looked stunned, and I felt her fierce reaction in my own small breast. Taking courage from the emotion rolling off of her, I yanked my arms out of my father's hands and ran to hide behind her. She reached back, tucking me close to her legs. I tried to hold still enough so Daddy would forget I existed.

"Don't you threaten me, Jay Janus," I could feel my mom tremble, but her voice was strong and unwavering. "I *will* call the police." My dad snapped out of his furious trance.

"Shelley, come here," he squatted to face me at my level. "Please?" he pleaded. "I didn't mean to scare you." I wouldn't budge. "Quit holding her, Denise!" he looked up at my mom. To draw his attention off her, I left her shadow and went to stand before him.

I SAT UP IN BED, my heart racing. I could hear a fleet of military choppers receding in the distance. Aghast, I tried to calculate how old I was when this scene took place. I couldn't have even been four; the diving board memory was about age four. I must have been three years old!

Hatred for my parents swirled in me, and the panic attack that followed was brutal.

When my tears dried, I was surprised to find myself staring in the bathroom mirror. I looked down. I was less surprised to see three round white pills nestled in my palm. I looked up again. My eyes were green, unlike both my parents' blue ones. I always thought my face looked like my dad's, but now I saw it: I was looking like my mom lately, too. Staring into the mashed up mask of my parents' faces, I filled a plastic cup with water from the sink faucet. I jiggled the pills in my palm, then returned two of them to the bottle. I looked back in the mirror.

"One is not going to kill you," I said disdainfully. I drank it down.

Lying in bed a few minutes later, trying to forget the nightmare memory, inspiration struck. I couldn't take the painkillers that'd been prescribed *before* I started psych meds, but there had to be some that were okay to take *with* them if prescribed by a knowledgeable doctor. I grinned against my pillow and snuggled myself tight under the heaped blankets. The thermostat was still set to tundra temps; I tried to turn it up the first night Ed was away but sweated till the sheets were sticky. I turned it back down rather than abandon the weighty protection of my many-layered covers. They were the only thing standing between the hand under the bed and me.

"SHELL, I'M SO SORRY," my dad was the one crying on the phone this time. It was another grey glue morning. I'd just repeated my story for him and Charlie. "I did this to you, didn't I? It's all my fault!" I could barely make out his self-tormented words.

"Dad," I held my tears in tight lockdown. "This isn't your fault. It's an illness, like the flu. My brain isn't working correctly, so I'm taking medication and looking into other treatments that will help it."

"Aw, Jay," Charlie cooed. "Shelley's not blaming you!"

"I've been a terrible dad! I'm sorry I let you down so many times. I'm sorry I've let all of you down so many times," he expanded his oft-repeated apology to encompass my stepmom and, presumably, my college-aged half-brother, who was not on the call. "I'm worthless. Everyone would be better off without me around!"

Charlie admonished, "Jay, don't say that," at the same time, I exclaimed, "That's not true, Dad!"

I continued, "I need you, and my kids need their grandfather. Michael needs his dad. Charlie needs you, too." I could hear him struggling to staunch the tears.

"I'm sorry, Shell," he said after a moment. "I don't want to talk about me. When do you go back to the doctor?" I told them the same things I'd told everyone else.

"Shell," Charlie said. "I'm sorry this is happening to you, but I'm very thankful you're out of that work environment. Give yourself time. I'll be praying for you!"

"Thanks, Charlie," I said. My dad choked up again.

"I'm sorry I wasn't around more when you were little, Pal," he said. "I'm sorry the business failed. I'm sorry…" his voice trailed off in tears.

"Dad, it's okay," I reassured him. "I'm going to be fine! You need to stop blaming yourself."

"Yeah," he said.

"Love you," he and Charlie said together.

"I love you guys, too," I hung up and stared out the window.

CHAPTER 13

Fifteen minutes ahead of time, I eased my car into a spot facing the coffee shop entrance. It was in the same strip mall as the hair salon and the drugstore with the nosy pharmacist. I peered inside. Lydia wasn't there yet. I left the engine running to keep the car toasty, closed my eyes, and reclined into the cushy headrest. It'd been a jam-packed few days since the maudlin call with my dad. I replayed select scenes in my mind.

"IF DOING SO MAKES you feel less anxious, then it is acceptable," Dr. Basu allowed. "But there's no science behind it."

"Dr. Drexler told me it's used in Stanford hospitals, so there must be some evidence it works!" I argued despite my own skepticism about the Reiki class for which I'd registered.

"Its being used is not proof of its efficacy," she sniffed. "Now, what about the walks?"

"I went on one five-mile hike," I announced proudly. She inhaled to speak, but I spoke first. "And I started taking group exercise classes at a local gym. I went to three of them since I saw you last!" Instead of the approval I anticipated, I felt doubt arising from the doctor.

"In the past ten days, you've done this?"

"Yes," I wanted to add, 'you stupid bitch,' but I managed not to.

"You've done this, yet you feel no improvement in your moods?" she squinted at me.

"I definitely feel a lift for an hour or two after exercising, but then, everything collapses in on me again," I tried to distill my experience into a formula. She made a note in my chart.

"I would like to add a second antidepressant. This one works differently," she explained some intricacies of the new drug.

I almost couldn't wait for her to finish before saying, "Can we go back for a second? I've had pain in my knee since I started vigorous exercise." I stifled a giggle, remembering Ed's eyebrows in bed. "It'll take more than ibuprofen to keep me going till I'm stronger. Is there something you can prescribe?"

"Is there swelling with this pain?" she looked concerned.

Gambling that she was more likely to help me if there were multiple symptoms, I said, "Yes, but only a little."

"If there's swelling, you need to see your orthopedic surgeon to rule out injury. You already have an appointment scheduled?" She tore two sheets off her prescription pad and held them across to me.

"Yes," I took the slips of paper, still hopeful.

"Those are refills for your existing prescriptions, plus the new one, Effexor. Follow the label instructions."

Dejected, I said, "My appointment with the surgeon isn't till next week."

"That is acceptable," Dr. Basu said, standing to show me out. "Until you're able to see him, exercise only when your knee is pain-free."

I opened my eyes to scan the coffee shop—still no Lydia. I should've asked if she drove the same car, I thought, gazing around the lot to see if she was lurking, like me. From this vantage point, I couldn't find her. I closed my eyes again.

"I'm sorry, I put the appointment on his calendar, I swear," I said to Barry. We made small talk while waiting for Ed, who had yet to read my fifteen reminder texts.

"Why don't we talk about whatever you wanted to discuss?" Barry sounded confused. "I'm sure Ed trusts you to deliver your shared message." In two decades, I'd never insisted that Ed be party to our financial planning phone calls.

"That's not the point," I said, just as my phone dinged. "I need him here, and he promised."

I read the text from Ed; "Got caught up in a client meeting. You still on with Barry?"

"GET ON THE FUCKING PHONE," I sent back.

"I can't. Walking down the hall to another meeting," he replied.

"Shelley?" asked Barry.

"Yeah, I'm still here. Texting with Ed, just a minute," I muted the phone, so I could cuss Ed out while I typed my reply.

"I REFUSE to finish this conversation with Barry unless you join the call NOW. Take five minutes from your client for a bathroom break and CALL ME NOW."

It took more than a minute for him to send back, "Can't. Gotta go. Will call after." I stared at the text until I was sure the rising panic would not cripple me. When I could, I unmuted the call.

"Barry?" I said. "Ed can't join because of a work emergency. Let me bring you up to speed," I retold my tale, tearless and wound tight with unspent anxiety. In the end, I said, "Our income will be cut by over a third. Pretty soon, we'll be adding to credit card balances instead of paying them down."

"How much credit card debt are you currently servicing?" he asked. I was so pissed at Ed for not being here for this part! I told Barry how much. He was silent. I scrambled to explain.

"We're working on it! We were making headway until the water main in the front yard disintegrated, and we ended up having to re-landscape," I caught my breath. "And, unfortunately, we'd already ordered a new shed before we knew I was going on leave. It's not returnable."

"Look, Shelley, you don't have to justify to me how you spend your money," Barry said kindly. "I always do what I can to make your family's life easier; your Nana took a chance on me when I was new in my industry, and I owe some of my success to her. But I wouldn't be doing my fiduciary duty if I didn't tell you that, as your financial advisor, I disapprove of this trend."

"I'm sorry," I winced at the gentle dressing-down. "I know it's a problem. With my going on leave like this, I think our lives will have to change significantly for the long-term. Ed and I started talking about me staying home and moving to someplace more affordable." I held my breath, expecting criticism.

"That's something we can work with," Barry brightened. "I know your mom is bothered that you can't spend more time with your kids," he dangled the bait and the stick in one neat package. "I'm going to recommend that she add some modified repayment provisions to the promissory note," he said. "But, I think she'll see her way to helping you." It felt like I could breathe again.

SOMEONE KNOCKED on the glass by my ear. I jumped so hard, the car rocked. I peeked out and wiped my brow in mock relief before I rolled down the window.

"Sorry I startled you," said Trina, my stylist. "I just

wanted to say, your hair is still stunning! Are you waiting for someone?"

"Yes, I'm meeting someone for coffee," I said.

"Oh, me, too!" Trina laughed. "Maybe I'll see you in there," she waved and stepped away from the car.

I rolled up the window, muttering under my breath, "Not if I can help it."

"WHAT IF I'M A LESBIAN?" I asked.

"What if you are?" asked Julia.

"Well, I don't think I am," I rebutted.

"Would it matter if you were?" she asked.

"I don't know," I sighed. "It seems like it'd be easier."

She scribbled in her black notebook before asking, "Easier than what?"

"Being bisexual seems so taboo," I said. "I think I'm bisexual!"

"Who told you it was taboo?" she probed. I thought about my best friend from freshman year of college and the way our friendship ended. I didn't want to talk about my sexuality anymore, so I changed the subject. This seemed to be how therapy worked. I brought something up and talked about it till I didn't want to anymore, while Julia listened and asked questions to keep me going for an hour.

"I don't think Dr. Basu likes me," I complained. "She won't prescribe what I need!"

"What do you mean, she won't?" Julia followed along.

"Well, I asked her for sleeping pills, and she put me off, for starters," I fussed. "And when I told her my knee hurts from the exercise she ordered, then asked for something more than ibuprofen to get me through, she ignored me! She gave me another antidepressant instead. I need sleep and exercise, not more psych drugs!"

Frustratingly, Julia asked, "Why do you think she gave you another antidepressant?"

"I don't know, I'm not a psychiatrist," I snapped. "I guess I have to find another doctor to fix my problems."

Julia checked the clock and said, "Well, I'm sorry to say I don't have prescribing powers in this state. You should ask Dr. Basu why she gave you another antidepressant if you don't know."

"What does it matter," I moaned. "Nothing gets better! Everything gets worse, and every day gets harder." Julia finished writing and clapped her notebook shut.

"Our time's up," she said. "I look forward to seeing you in a couple days."

My phone rang. It was 7:58 p.m.

"Hello?" I answered.

"Hey," Ed greeted. "I called home, and the sitter answered. She said you're out for coffee with a friend?"

"Yeah," I'd rehearsed my alibi. "Gen and I are getting coffee at the shop over by the salon," I said. "I'm waiting in my car for her to show. She's going to tell me more about learning Reiki."

"Oh, fun," Ed said. "Tell her to say hi to Aaron for me!"

"I'll do that," I promised. "What'd you call for? Everything okay?"

"I called to tell you I got on a flight tomorrow afternoon instead of tomorrow night. I'll be home early enough to get the kids from school!"

"Oh," I said. "That's great. The kids will be thrilled."

"I talked to my parents," Ed said. "Why didn't you call them after Eddie's practice Tuesday? I told them you would." I tried to remember Tuesday night. I couldn't. I figured it was probably spent drunk, watching movies.

"Because I just didn't want to, Ed," I said impatiently.

"They want to support you, Shell," he said. "You can talk to them, you know. It's not like talking to *your* parents."

"It's not that easy!" I felt badgered. "Sometimes, I don't even want to talk to my therapist, let alone your mom and dad."

"Well, I wish you would try harder with them. They just want to help." I lost my cool.

"Well, *I* wish *you* would try harder to show up when I schedule business calls for us!" I'd planned to save this conversation until he was home, but the hypocrisy was unbearable.

"Shell, I already said I was sorry," he sighed. "You handled everything with Barry just fine. You didn't even need me!"

"But, Ed, *you promised*," I hissed. "I'm tired of you lying to me!" I exaggerated the injury.

"It's not a lie," he protested. "Just because I forget an appointment or have to miss a commitment because of work doesn't mean I'm lying."

"What's the difference?" I asked. "The end result is the same; my feelings are hurt because you said you'd do something and you didn't. I see no distinction."

"Shell, I said I'm sorry. Are you going to keep beating me up over this forever?" I wanted to sulk and say yes, but I didn't. I'd spied Lydia driving into the lot. In the side-view mirror, I watched her park a few rows behind me.

"Ed, we can talk about this later," I said in an even tone. "Gen's here. I don't want to keep her waiting."

"All right, call me later to say goodnight?"

"Yeah, I'll do that," I promised. "Love you, talk to you later."

"Love you, bye."

"Sorry for the wait," the cashier deposited our drinks on the table between Lydia and me. "The barista didn't see my note that a member of management was on-premises," she fretted.

Lydia deadpanned, "You won't get fired, as long as it's the right temp." The cashier looked worried. "I'm teasing!" Lydia said. "I'm sure it's fine. Thanks for bringing it over." The girl walked away, looking relieved.

"That was cruel!" I leaned across the table and

wagged a finger at Lydia. "Shame on you for using your superior position to torment her," I laughed.

Lydia cracked a devilish grin, took a sip, and asked, "So, what happened last time?" We'd been comparing superficial notes about the weather and our lives until the coffee arrived.

I squirmed and said, "I'm really sorry for the way I ditched you."

"I was let down and kind of embarrassed," she said. "I went into a serious funk. I had to start antidepressants again. And I'd been off them since Denny was born!" I looked down into my cup, remorseful. "Don't feel bad, though. Bill and I went to couples' therapy. We learned to communicate better. We got along so well, I even got pregnant! That's how Nash was conceived." I was relieved she didn't hold my rogue behavior against me.

"I never thought my actions would be so hurtful to you," I said. "I just—" I stopped.

"Got cold feet?" she supplied the phrase I was missing.

"Yeah, I guess you could say that," I looked up from the cinnamon-speckled surface of my coffee to her cinnamon-speckled eyes. She smiled playfully.

"Your cold feet got me a bonus baby, a better relationship with my husband, and a long-term girlfriend, to boot! I more than forgive you." I wanted her to continue; I loved her raspy voice.

"Tell me about your girlfriend," I said.

"Ex-girlfriend," she corrected. "T and I broke up a month ago."

"Oh," I was baffled. "I saw pictures on your Facebook page from a couple years ago of you and a woman named Tasha," I said. "Is that who you're talking about?"

"No, that's a different ex," Lydia looked pained. "Tasha and I only dated for two months. It didn't end well. She had issues."

"I see," I said.

"I'm talking about Tanya, my most recent girlfriend. We dated for two years. She and Bill got to be close friends. I think he misses her more than I miss her!" she laughed. With my empath sense, I picked up conflicting emotions.

I decided it was safe to ask, "So Bill is still okay with your having a girlfriend?"

"Oh, yes, he's very enthusiastic these days," she said. "He's cheering me on to find the next one." I felt the confusion on my face. Lydia saw it and clarified, "He misses how horny I am when I have a side piece." I felt my face flare up like wildfire.

"Side piece? Isn't that offensive?"

"No," she assured me. "Our marriage counselor taught us to be truthful and forthright with each other. Since we thrive on shared humor, we started calling my girlfriends side-pieces. It's kind of sexy to mock-fight with your husband about your side piece when she's on her way over to pick you up for a date. The sex we have after a night like that is incredible," she rhapsodized. I peeked around us to see if anyone was listening; Lydia's distinctive voice carried.

"I wouldn't know," I said. "Ed and I have been a little…slow…in the sex department lately."

"Is that so?" she leaned over the table toward me. "Maybe you and Ed should consider an open marriage, like Bill and I have."

"What's that mean, an open marriage?" I asked. I'd done a little digging about the rise of polyamory and the expected wave of 'throuples' in progressive San Francisco. Reading about it paled in comparison to getting the goods from someone brave enough to take the plunge.

"In our case, it means that I get to have a girlfriend with Bill's blessing. What I'm really looking for is a wife, to be honest. I realized a few months ago, I need both a husband and a wife. I'd like to find someone to move in and parent alongside Bill and me." Well, that put me right out. I wasn't about to leave my husband for another husband, AND a wife! Lydia continued, "For Bill, I don't know, it's different. I want him to get a girlfriend, so we can swap if everyone's into it," my eyes raced around the room again, afraid someone would overhear. "He hasn't found anyone suitable yet. He has more refined tastes than I do!" she laughed loudly now.

"Michelle," I jumped to see Trina standing beside our table. "I thought I'd say goodnight," she leaned down and offered her cheek for me to claim a continental-style kiss.

"Trina!" I hopped to my feet. "Meet my…friend, Lydia," I gestured to Lydia, who watched us closely.

"Charmed, I'm sure," Trina held out a bejeweled

hand for Lydia to shake. It looked like Lydia might bite it off instead. "I'm Michelle's stylist," Trina nodded at my head.

"Pleased to meet you," Lydia took the proffered hand, turned the backside up, and actually kissed it! Trina erupted in delighted laughter.

"What a cad," she winked at Lydia. "I'll let you two get back to your conversation," I thought I detected air quotes around the word 'conversation.' I felt my face burn. "See you in a few weeks," Trina looked at me knowingly. "Enjoy your evening!" I awkwardly accepted her kiss-kiss-kiss on alternating cheeks and sat back down.

"That's who made your hair look so good, huh?" Lydia watched Trina sashay out the door in her Bohemian garb.

"Yeah, she's pretty artistic, huh?" I admired.

"You're pretty pretty," she said to me pointedly.

"Thanks," I blushed, thinking this was way too easy.

"I want to know something," Lydia leaned toward me. "Did you ever actually tell your husband you were seeing me?"

"No, I didn't," I admitted. "I was so unsure of myself, I didn't want to drag him into my indecision."

"I can accept that," Lydia sat back. "I just wish I'd known sooner, like when we were still in contact."

"All I can say, once again, is that I'm sorry." Lydia nodded and took a sip of coffee.

"Did you email me in hopes we'd get back together?" she asked.

"Well," I dragged my heels. "I don't know if it's so much that," I didn't want to seem desperate, but I also didn't want to endanger my chance to sate this corrupt curiosity. "It's more along the lines of, I felt there might be unfinished business between us." I swear if Lydia had a tail, it would've twitched as she drank her frothy coffee, cream for a much bigger cat.

"Unfinished business, like what?" she pressed.

"I'm not sure yet," I dodged.

"Huh," she put her cup down in its saucer. "You want another?" she pointed at my empty cup.

"Sure," I said, checking my watch. "I have about an hour left till the babysitter has to go."

"Babysitter?" she put her hand up to wave the cashier over to our table again.

"Yeah," I told her about Ed's trip and its extension. "He's gonna be disappointed that I'm planning to attend back-to-back classes at my new gym tomorrow when he gets home," I paused while Lydia ordered from the girl standing beside our table. I felt conspicuous and a little rude; it wasn't a full-service coffee shop. "Is it okay for her to stop her job and serve us like that?" I asked after she walked away.

"I'm a store manager," Lydia looked proud. "There's an unspoken rule that staff is to give visiting managers extra attention. It's sort of a competition; we compare notes on district calls." I nodded. "So, what gym do you go to?" Lydia asked. I told her about Utopia Fitness.

"I really like Afro-Belly-Boogie, but Genevieve, who introduced me to Utopia, she prefers Zumba."

"Genevieve?" Lydia asked sharply.

173

"Yeah, she's the daughter-in-law of our former next-door neighbors," I explained the twisty acquaintance.

"I've been looking to join a gym lately," Lydia said. "Maybe I'll check out Utopia."

"Sure," I agreed, thinking how silly it'd be for her to drive all the way from the Peninsula for a workout.

"You must be working from home a lot if you're going to the gym on weekdays," Lydia guessed. "Are you at the same job?" I hesitated. "I saw the same employer as before listed on your Facebook page, so I assumed," she explained.

"It's a long story," I rechecked my watch. "And I have to be home on time. Our babysitter has a final tomorrow; I promised I wouldn't be late."

"I want to hear your story," Lydia coaxed. "But if you don't want to," she shrugged.

"It's not that," I said. "I want to—" I stopped and turned the tables. "What about *your* job? You were at one of those sweet companies everyone clamors to get into. Why's that no longer the case?" I smiled at the barista who was delivering our second round.

"Thanks," Lydia said to her. "I can't wait to brag about Moe's staff on the call next week." The barista grinned excitedly.

"What's up with that?" I asked when she retired to her station.

"They get perks when they get a good mention," she explained. "Moe spiffs this store each five bucks."

"Ah, I see," I waited for her to say more.

"You asked about my job," she stirred her new coffee thoughtfully. "After you disappeared, things were rough. I held on until they laid off a bunch of us in the real estate crash. By then, the last thing I wanted was to see the inside of another tech firm. I decided to return to my roots, slinging coffee. I started as an assistant and was made manager within a year. I hope to be moved up to district next year," I loved the confidence in her voice. I wished I felt that way about my career! "It's your turn," she said.

"Okay," I said. "But please don't think worse of me for what I'm about to say," I delivered my well-rehearsed speech. I was candid about the role my sexual curiosity played with Lydia, unlike with my earlier audiences. I didn't mean to tell her so much, but I could say things to her that I couldn't tell my therapist. "So," I concluded, "I emailed you, and here we are. I don't want to drag you into my drama. I'm sorry if it seems that way, especially after the way I treated you last time!"

"Don't mention it," Lydia set down the cup she'd held suspended in the air during the final minutes of my story. "I'm happy you found me," she began, but my phone rang. It was the babysitter.

"Crap!" I saw the time. "I'm already five minutes late." Lydia watched while I apologized into the phone and promised to be home in a half-hour. It reminded me of standing in the driveway with her while I lied to Ed.

When I hung up, she prompted, "So, you were saying, you have questions about your sexuality and marriage?"

"Not about my marriage!" I rushed to clear that misconception. "Ed and I are soulmates, you know. You must remember the story I told you about how we met?"

"How could anyone forget *that* story?" she rolled her eyes and nodded. "It's like a fairy tale. Pretty hard to compete with." A little glow started in my heart. She was thinking about competing for my affections!

"Ed's an amazing husband," I said. "I'm lucky to have him. The problem is, I think I might like women, too. But I still haven't done anything about finding out."

"Wait," Lydia burst out. "You mean you still never had a girlfriend?"

"Nope," I confirmed. The preying-cat look was back.

"Are you looking for one now?" she purred and peeked at me through lowered lashes. I laughed at her exaggerated manner.

"I need to tell Ed first this time," I'd thought long and hard about how to succeed in this foray. "I don't want a replay of the lying and hiding."

"You've already met someone, haven't you?" the fiery Lydia from the red couch of the hotel lobby made her entrance. I silently snickered.

"I might've," I stoked her jealousy. "But we have to see where things go. She's been burned before." The look on Lydia's face was pure gold. It was envy and rage and hope and doubt all wrapped up in one unbearably ugly-beautiful mask. I continued, "Hey, Lydia, I've really gotta go. My babysitter will never work for me again if I don't get there in ten minutes. Plus, I have those classes at Utopia tomorrow," I dangled the bait she seemed likely to take based on our earlier conversation. "I need to rest tonight, so I'm not dead on my feet. I wouldn't wanna fall and break anything!"

"I can't go tomorrow," Lydia blurted. "When's the next one you'll be at?" Now, I was the cat licking the cream.

"Tuesday at 6 p.m.?" I offered.

"Perfect," Lydia stood up and dusted herself off briskly. "I'll be there."

"See you then," I confirmed. She held the door open for me on the way out.

"Thanks for visiting!" yelled the cashier and barista in unison. Lydia waved at them, then came to stand beside me at my car door. I turned to face her. She leaned in. The absence of wine dregs on her breath disconcerted me. Our lips met. Hers were soft and warm, just like all the fantasies I harbored.

CHAPTER 14

September 2015

For a long time, we lay close together on your bed, atop crumpled white blankets. The pillows had been cast to the ground during our passionate embraces. Unlike with Ed or my other lovers, I enjoyed lying beside you in our afterglow. The heat radiating off your skin felt good; it meant I wasn't alone. You seemed to enjoy it, too, tracing your fingertips absently over your chest and staring into the ceiling fan that spun lazily overhead.

"When d'you have to get ready for work?" I asked. You checked the alarm clock.

"Few minutes," you said. "You need anything?" I shook my head no. We lapsed back into companionable silence. Pretty soon, you sighed and pushed onto your elbows.

"Is it time?" I asked.

"Yeah," you said. I rolled over after nudging Sissy out of my way. You started the shower while I re-clasped the hot pink lace bra. This was the longest stretch of time we'd spent in each other's company, I realized. I checked my heart. Still no ache. Wearing a bath towel wrapped around your waist, you and Sissy escorted me to the front door.

"Text you soon?" you said.

"Yeah," I said. "I'll be busy with the kids the whole rest of the day, so whenever."

"Okay, thanks again, baby," you leaned over to peck me on the lips. I forced myself not to wrinkle my nose.

DRIVING HOME over the Columbia River on the I-5 bridge, I caught a whiff of the perfume that permeated your home, clinging to my clothes. I decided I would definitely ditch you. Enjoying intimacy with a lover was not on my list of allowable activities. I felt a weird attachment to you where I did not want to feel anything, ever. Even the familiarity of your dog unnerved me! I decided I'd text you in the morning; today, we had back-to-school festivities.

As a PTO volunteer, my assignment for the evening was to operate the refreshment table. A shiver of panic passed through me. I checked the time. Too long since my last dose. I scrabbled in my purse, focus wandering from the road. Someone honked. I jerked into my own lane and flipped them off, clutching the pill bottle behind the bird. I couldn't afford another accident! I held off opening the bottle till after I left the narrow bridge lanes.

"Hɪ, Mᴏᴍ," Eddie pulled open the back door and got in. I'd caught up with him walking toward home after being dropped off by the middle school bus.

"Hi, sweetheart," I said. "How was school today?" He launched into a story about Pokémon battles in the lunchroom. I couldn't keep track of it all, so I smiled and let him talk. Eddie scooted over to let Elsie take his place when we glided to the elementary school curb.

"Hello, sugar," I greeted her after she climbed in.

"Hi, Momma," she said. "I can't wait for tonight!"

"Did you memorize the rest of your lyrics?" I asked. Elsie was singing welcome songs in the cafeteria with all the third-grade classes.

"Yes, Momma," she said. "My favorite song is—"

"I don't want to go to back-to-school night," Eddie cut her off. "I'd rather go to Augie's house."

"Eddie, do not interrupt," I commanded. "Elsie was talking."

"She was done," he argued.

"No, I wasn't," Elsie corrected him. "Mom, can't he stay home tonight with Dad?" I sighed. Eddie's current mix of ADHD meds didn't seem to be working well anymore.

"Eddie, Augie and his family will be at back-to-school night," I said. "Remember? He has a brother in Elsie's grade."

"Cool," he said. "I can hang out with him!"

"But, I want you to listen to me sing all the songs at least once!" Elsie said.

"Boring," her brother yawned.

"Mom," Elsie appealed to me. "Eddie said he's not going to listen to all my songs!" Having been raised an only child, I did not understand this sibling interplay. I just knew my nerves couldn't take it today.

"Quit arguing!" I snapped. "Eddie said no such thing, Elsie. He's teasing you."

"Am not," I caught Eddie mouthing at Elsie in the rearview mirror.

"Edward!" the sound of my voice filled the car. "If you don't stop it now, you will not be going to back-to-school night! You'll be grounded instead."

That effectively ended the argument.

THE NEXT MORNING, I woke before my alarm. I had a massive headache, and my mouth was sawdust-dry. Back-to-school night had not gone well. Or perhaps it had gone too well. In an attempt to quell my agoraphobic worries, I'd overindulged. I remembered taking extra Xanax and Klonopin. I took one Valium, I was pretty sure. Had I also taken the Ativan? Whatever I took, I barely remembered any of the night.

I checked my phone. You'd messaged me some twenty minutes earlier.

"Thank you for yesterday. Can you meet same time next week?" I was surprised. We'd only been seeing each other every other week or two. I checked the rest of my messages. As I thought, I'd promised the same morning next week to Stan. He was another lover I was letting in a second time. I had a feeling he was destined to become a regular. He lived less than a mile away, we saw eye-to-eye on everything, and our wit matched like two perfectly opposed rapiers. We even drove the same model and color of car.

A message arrived from my Canadian hockey player.

"Just getting to bed," it read. "Lunch?"

"Time?" I replied.

"1:30," he sent. I had therapy in the late morning and nothing else planned.

"Basil," I sent one of our code words. He didn't reply. We'd been doing this so long, we both knew what the other left unsaid. I switched back to your messages.

"I'm sorry," I typed, "but this isn't going to work anymore. Good-bye." I stared at the words.

I backspaced over them and sent, "Yes."

To be continued…

ABOUT THE AUTHORS

Michelle was prophesied by her first-grade teacher to be an Author. Already a logophile and voracious consumer of the written word, Michelle cherished the idea. During her early years, she penned award-winning poetry and short stories, striving to give voice to the story she knew she held in her Soul. Michelle's writing took a decades-long hiatus while she pursued a career in the corporate finance world. Now, she knows why her intuition whispered to hold off on writing. The Twin Flame story is the story she was waiting to tell the world.

Justin followed an early path very different from that of his Twin Flame. Born into an evangelistic Christian sectarian family, he left his parents' home at age 18 to begin a 30-year career serving others in retail management. After gaining exposure to the world beyond the cult of his youth, Justin declared himself Apostate and was cast out by the community that raised him. Always a Searcher, he pursued religious understanding and clarity, never knowing that what he truly sought was his Twin Flame instead of a man-made religion. Today, Reunified with his Twin, he's ready to tell his story to the world.

As Twin Flame Warriors and Awakening Navigators, Michelle & Justin offer spiritual guidance counseling to those who seek their true path. If you know you've been looking for something, but aren't sure what it is or where to find it, contact them. Chances are, they can help.

∞

Made in the USA
Monee, IL
17 October 2021

80204436R00111